DS

El Cortijo

ISLA MONTAÑA CLARA   ISLA GRACIOSA

LANZAROTE

Pedro Barba
Mirador
del Río
Caleta del Sebo   Orzola
Punta del Roque   *Punta del Palo*
Maguez
Punta Guerra   Caleta   Haria
Punta Prieta   de Famara
Punta los Cuchillos   Sóo   Guatiza
Punta del Paletón   Tinajo   Teguise   *Punta Abrigada*
Tao
Punta de la Ensenada   Mancha Blanca   San Bartolomé   Taiche
El Golfo   Costa Teguise
Yaiza   Tias
Femes   Puerto
del Carmen   **ARRECIFE**
Pta. Pechiguera   *Punta Gorda*
Playa
Blanca   *Punta del Papagayo*

Punta Lola   *Faro de Martiño*
Faro del Tostón   Corralejo
Lajares
Casas de Taca
Punta de Paso Chico   La Oliva   *La Puntilla*
La Matilla   Guisguey
Los Molinos
Casillas
del Angel   **PUERTO
DEL ROSARIO**
Punta de los Caletones
Puerto   Betancuria   Antigua   *Punta Gonzalo*
de la Peña
Las Salinas   Pájara   Tuineje
Fayagua   Las Casitas
Tesegerague
Punta de las Goteras   *Ensenada de Jacomar*
Tarajalejo   Gran Tarajal
Punta Paloma   *Punta del Caracol*
Matas Blancas
nta Pesebre
Cofete   Risco del Paso   # FUERTEVENTURA
de Jandía
Morro del Jable

Atlantic Ocean

Juan-Alberto Rodríguez Pérez

VISIT

EXOTIC FLORA OF THE
CANARY ISLANDS

EVEREST

Author: Juan-Alberto Rodríguez Pérez
Professor of Gardening and Landscape Gardening, Department of
Agricultural Science, University of La Laguna. Ex-curator of La Orotava
Botanical Gardens.

Photographs: Author and Oliviero Daidola

Diagrams: Gerardo Rodera

Cover Design: Alfredo Anievas

Digital image processing: Marcos R. Méndez

Translation: Bénedict School, Edward Barreto, Pilar de Valdelomar
and Koiné

THIRD EDITION
© Juan-Alberto Rodríguez Pérez
© EDITORIAL EVEREST, S. A.
Carretera León-La Coruña, km 5 – LEÓN
ISBN: 84-241-3552-0
National Book Catalogue Number: LE. 64-2001
Printed in Spain

EDITORIAL EVERGRÁFICAS, S. L.
Carretera León-La Coruña, km 5
LEÓN (Spain)

INTRODUCTION

The sea voyages of exploration initiated from the C15th onwards by Spaniards and Portuguese, thereafter to be continued by other nations (English, French, etc) led to the discovery of new lands and consequently of new plants.

Due to their geographical position, the Canary Islands were an obligatory stopover for ships on their way to America, Africa, Asia and Australia. This soon gave rise to the arrival of plant species from the tropics and subtropics, which easily took to the benign climate of the islands.

The setting up of La Orotava Botanical Gardens, on the island of Tenerife in the late C18th gave a real boost to the introduction of plants from Spain's overseas possessions, many of which have now become incorporated into Canary gardening.

Canary emigrations to America, the last during this century being to Cuba and Venezuela, in that order, helped greatly to keep up a steady flow of exotic plants towards the islands.

Canary gardens are full of exotic species of great beauty, coming from all corners of the earth. The wonderful world of palm trees is represented by species as handsome as the Cuban Royal Palm *(Roystonea regia)*, the Australian Bangalow or Piccabean Palm *(Archontophoenix cunninghamiana)* and the Chilean Wine Palm *(Jubea chilensis)*. The prime examples of trees with striking blossom are the Flame of the Forest *(Delonix regia)* from Madagascar, the Jacaranda *(Jacaranda mimosifolia)* from South America and the Tulip Tree of *(Spathodea campanulata)* from Gabon in tropical Africa. Island gardens are embellished by ornamental species like Hibiscus *(Hibiscus rosa-sinensis)* from Asia, the Croton *(Codiaeum variegatum var. Pictum)* from the Moluccas and Malaysia, and the Barbados Pride or Poincaina *(Caesalpinia pulcherrima)* from the West Indies. The most well-known and widespread climbers are the Bougainvilleas, with several cultivars in red, violet, white or brick red. Other eyecatching climbers are the Flame Vine *(Pyrostegia venusta)* from Brazil, and the Gold Cup *(Solandra maxima)* from Mexico. The most popular of the perennials is the Bird of Paradise *(Strelitzia reginae)*, which has been used in tourist campaigns as a symbol of the islands but is in fact a South African species. Other highly attractive species are Balisier *(Heliconia bihai)* from the West Indies and northern South America, the Common Agapanthus or Blue Baby *(Agapanthus praecox. Ssp. Orientalis)* from South Africa and the Shell Ginger *(Alpinia zerumbet)* from east Asia.

All these plants, and many more that are too numerous to mention, form part of our daily life. They adorn our streets, avenues, parks and gardens, playing an important role in cutting down air pollution and in controlling the temperature and air humidity. They are fellow members of our community. It therefore behoves us to get to know them better, so as to be able to assess the function they perform, thereby increasing our respect and affection for them.

This book aims to provide both islanders and visiting tourists with brief, practical information on nearly two hundred species of palms, trees, shrubs, climbers and perennials that may be admired in the gardens, squares and parks of the islands.

The species are included in alphabetical order of their scientific names. The description of each one includes the scientific name, the family it belongs to, geographical distribution, common name, morphological characteristics, growing conditions, exploitation by man, use in gardening, flowering or fruiting period and form of propagation. The flowering and fruiting information corresponds to the Puerto de la Cruz (Tenerife), a spot with probably the best climate in the world; moreover, its gardens, including the Botanical Gardens, display most of the species included in this book.

At the end of the book there is a glossary to explain botanical terminology to those who are unfamiliar with it.

THE AUTHOR

ACALYPHA WILKESIANA

Acalypha wilkesiana. Müll. Arg.
Family: *Euphorbiaceae*.
Propagation: usually by cuttings.

Common name: COPPER LEAR
Geographical distribution: Pacific Islands.

Monoecious, evergreen shrub, up to 4.5 m high. Leaves alternate, simple, ovate or elliptical, acuminate, serrate, greenish bronze in colour, mottled with red, copper or purple, up to 20 cm long or more. Small flowers in reddish spikes up to 10 cm long. Fruits in capsules.
Cv. Obovata. Leaves obovate, emarginated, with pink margins.
Tolerates most soils, preferring sunny spots although it withstands partial shade. Fast growing.
It is used in gardening individually, in groups and for hedges.

Acalypha wilkesiana.

Acokanthera oblongifolia.

ACOKANTHERA OBLONGIFOLIA

Acokanthera oblongifolia (Hochst.) Codd. [*A. spectabilis* (Sond.) Hook f.]
Family: *Apocynaceae*.
Flowering period: autumn-spring.

Geographical distribution: South Africa.
Propagación: seeds.

Evergreen shrub often seen reaching heights of 6 m. Opposite, ovate to elliptical leaves, leathery and shiny, up to 12 cm long. White flowers up to 1.8 cm in diameter, clustered in corymbs with jasmine-like scent. Berry fruits, ellipsoidal, globose, purple-blackish, with one or two seeds.
It prefers good soils, moist and partly shaded.
All the parts of this plant are poisonous. Its sap is used in South Africa by some tribes of natives to poison their arrows. It also has medicinal properties.
It is used in gardening both in isolation or in groups.

4

AGAPANTHUS PRAECOX

Agapanthus praecox. Willd. ssp. *orientalis* (Leighton) Leighton [*Agapanthus orientalis* Leighton].
Common name: COMMON AGAPANTHUS.
Geographical distribution: South Africa.
Propagation: by seeds and division.
Family: *Liliaceae.*
Flowering period: spring-summer.

Agapanthus praecox.

Perennial herbaceous plant, rhizomatous. Leaves basal, strap-shaped, caniculate, arched, up to 60 cm long and 6.5 cm wide. Blue flowers grouped in an umbel containing up to 110 flowers. Funnel-shaped corolla up to 5 cm in diameter. With a floral scape up to 105 cm long. Fruits in capsules. Prefers rich soil and abundant water. Can Live in bright sun as well as in shade.
Used in gardening to make up groups. It can also be planted in flower pots and the flowers used as cut flowers.

ALBIZIA JULIBRISSIN

Albizia julibrissin Durazz.
Common name: SILK TREE.
Flowering period: spring-summer.
Family: *Leguminosae.*
Geographical distribution: Iran through Japan.
Propagation: seeds.

Albizia julibrissin.

Deciduous tree up to 12 m high. Bipinnate leaves up to 30 cm long and at times longer. Oblong-curved folioles, up to 18 mm long, with the midvein located near one of the edges. Pink flowers in capitula grouped at ends of twigs. Fruits in pods up to 15 cm long.
It prefers siliceous soils and is resistant to drought, and to temperature as low as −10º C. It is seen in parks and gardens as well as urban avenues.

5

ALEURITES MOLUCCANA

Aleurites moluccana (L.) Willd [*A. triloba* J. R. Forst. et G. Forst.]
Common name: CANDLENUT TRRE.
Family: *Euphorbiaceae.*
Geographical distribution: Asia and Pacific Islands.
Flowering period: autumn.
Propagation: seeds and stem cutting.

Evergreen tree that grows up to 18 m high. Large, ovate, often angular or lobate leaves. Petioles up to 35 cm long. Blades up to 23 cm long. Small whitish flowers grouped in cymes. Globose fruits, up to 5 cm in diameter, with 1 or 2 large seeds with approximately 60% oil.
This tree grows on most soils and under most conditions as long as there is abundant water. It grows fast. In Tenerife it is both seen on the coast and inland, growing perfectly in La Laguna. It is cultivated in tropical countries to extract the oil from its seeds used in varnishes and as fuel. It is also used as a shade tree.

ALLAMANDA CATHARTICA

Allamanda cathartica L. Cv. Hendersonii.
Common name: GOLDEN TURMPET.
Family: *Apocynaceae.*
Flowering period:
summer-autumn-early winter.
Propagation: by cuttings.

A woody, climbing plant, evergreen. Leaves opposite or in verticils of 3-4, entire, coriaceous, oblanceolate to elliptical-oblong, up to 12 cm long; dark green, glossy above and paler beneath. Hermaphrodite flowers, grouped in cymes with few flowers. Funnel-shaped corolla, yellow in colour with brown striation on the inside, five-lobed, up to 8 cm long and 8 cm in diameter. The flower buds appear dyed with brown. Fruits in globate, spiny capsules.
It accepts most soils. Needs a sunny location, abundant water and an appropriate fertilization for better flowering. Slow growing. Sensitive to frost. Resistant to drought.
In gardening it is used to cover walls, pergolas, etc. and also in pots.

Allamanda cathartica Cv. Hendersonii.

Aleurites moluccana.

6

ALLAMANDA NERIIFOLIA

Allamanda neriifolia Hook.
Family: *Apocynaceae.*
Flowering period: almost year-round.

Geographical distribution: South America.
Propagation: by seeds and cuttings.

An evergreen shrub, sometimes with scandent branches, up to 1.5 m high. Leaves entire, in verticils of 2-5 leaves, elliptical or oblong, acuminate, up to 16 cm long. Very short petiole. Hermaphrodite flowers, clustered in sparsely flowered cymes. Funnel-shaped corolla, yellow in colour with yellow-reddish striation in the throat, up to 4 cm in diameter and about 5 cm long. Tube with a wide base. Fruits in globate, spiny capsules.
Little demanding about soil. It prefers a sunny location, abundant water and an appropriate fertilization to give good flowering. Slow growing. Resistant to drought.
Used in gardening to cover walls, etc. Also as a potted plant.

Allamanda Neriifolia.

ALPINIA ZERUMBET

Alpinia zerumbet (Pers.) B.L. Burtt et R.M.Sm
[*A. speciosa* (J.C. Wendl.) K. Schum.].
Common name: GINGER SHELL.
Family: *Zingiberaceae.*
Geographical distribution: East Asia.
Flowering period: nearly year-round.
Propagation: by seeds and division.

Perennial, herbaceous plant, rhizomatous, with numerous stems, up to 3.5 m high. Simple, lanceolate leaves with pubescent margins. Limbs up to 75 cm long and 15 cm wide. Sheathing petioles. Hermaphrodite flowers grouped in pendulous paniclesat the end of the stems. Three-lobed corolla, white with rosaceous tones at the tip. Labium-shaped staminode, yellow with spots and red striation, up to 5 cm long. Fruits in capsules.
It prefers rich souls with abundant moisture and a slightly shady location. The dry stems must be cut off at ground level in order to favour the budding of new sprouts.
Used in gardening to form groups.

Alpinia zerumbet.

7

Araucaria heterophylla.

ARAUCARIA HETEROPHYLLA

Araucaria heterophylla (Salisb.) Franco. **Common name:** NORFOLK PINE.
Family: *Araucariaceae.*   **Geographical distribution:** Island of Norfolk.
Propagation: seed, stem cutting and grafting.

Evergreen tree that can be seen reaching 60 m. Verticillate, horizontal
branches. The young needles are pointed and curved inwards. The adult
needles are lance-shaped or ovate-triangular, imbricate. Globular, feminine
cones, 12-15 cm in diameter and lengthwise alate seeds.
It grows on most soils and can grow quite close to the sea. It prefers sunny
or semishaded areas. It grows fast.
This tree is cultivated as a decorative plant; its use as a garden species is
restricted to large gardens and parks because the large roots constitute a
danger to nearby buildings.

Archontophoenix cunninghamiana.

ARCHONTOPHOENIX CUNNINGHAMIANA

Archontophoenix cunninghamiana (H. Wendl.) H. Wendl. et Drude.
Family: *Palmae.*
Geographical distribution: Australia.

Common name: PICCABEAN PALM.
Propagation: seeds.

Monoecious palm measuring up to 20 m high, with a sleek, ringed trunk.
Pinnate leaves up to 3 m long. Branched inflorescences beneath the leaves
with lilac flowers. Globular red fruits approximately 1.2 cm in diameter.
It grows on humid, rich soils, semishaded, although it can grow in open or
shaded spaces. It withstands strong winds and is fairly resistant to the cold. In
Tenerife it can be seen growing as high up as of La Laguna.
This palm is used in gardening, to form avenues, groups or as a free-standing
tree. It is also used in interior decoration.

ARISTOLOCHIA GIGANTEA

Aristolochia gigantea Mart. et Zucc., not Hook.
Family: *Aristolochiaceae.*
Geographical distribution: Brazil   **Flowering period:** almost year-round.
Propagation: by seeds, stem and root cutting and air layering.

Evergreen climbing shrub. Leaves entire, cordate, obtuse, with lengthwise petioles, up to 12 cm long. Hermaphrodite flowers, solitary, axillar, pendulouos from long peduncles. Perianth made up of a doubled, oblong-ovoid tube opening into a obcordiform-ovate limb, with purple spots on yellowish background, up to 50 cm long and about 40 cm wide. Fruit capsular.
Not particular about soil. It prefers a sunny location. Fast growing. Used in gardening to cover walls, pergolas, etc.

Aristolochia gigantea.

ARTOCARPUS ALTILIS

Artocarpus altilis (Parkins.) Fosb. [*A. incisus* L.f.]
Family: *Moraceae.*   **Common name:** BREAD-FRUIT TREE.
Geographical distribution: Malasia.   **Propagation:** seeds, stem cutting and root cutting.

Evergreen tree, monoecious, reaching over 15 m high. Large, ovate, pinnate-lobate, leathery leaves up to 90 cm long, dark green above, paler beneath. Male flowers grouped in clustered spikes up to 30 cm long. Female flowers in subglobular capitula. Round, muricate fruits, yellowish when ripe, up to 20 cm in diameter and made up of achenes grouped in a syncarp.
This tree prefers well drained, humid soils. It has a deep root system and needs to grow in hot areas.
This is a very ornamental species of tree, profusely used in gardens in

Artocarpus altilis.

tropical countries. It is also cultivated for its fruit, which can substitute bread when baked. The fruits are rich in carbohydrates and in vitamins A, B and C. The seeds are edible when roasted, and the wood has been used to make canoes. The best quality trees of this species do not give seeds. The breadfruit tree was introduced in tropical America to feed the black slaves. However, it did not prove successful, for other tropical plants such as the banana, yucca, etc., offered superior fruit that is easier and quicker to grow.

ARTOCARPUS HETEROPHYLLUS

Artocarpus heterophyllus Lam. [A. *integrifolius* auct. non. L.f.]
Famila: *Moraceae.*   **Geographical distribution:** India through the Malaysian Pinisula.
Common name: JACKFRUIT. **Propagation:** seeds and stem cutting.

Artocarpus heterophyllus.

Evergreen tree up to 15 m high. Entire, elliptical to obovate leaves up to 20 cm long, dark green above, paler beneath. Very small male flower grouped in cylindrical spikes or mace-shaped, up to 10 cm long. Female flowers in capitula. Elongated fruits, up to 60 cm long, consisting of achenes grouped in a yellowish-greenish syncarp when ripe. The fruits grow on the older branches and on the trunk, sometimes weighing 15-20 kilograms.
This tree requires rich, deep, humid soils with plenty of sun. It grows fast and is difficult to transplant.
The ripe fruits have an unpleasant smell, but the pulp tastes rather like a banana in taste and it is eaten raw, cooked or fried, and it is used to make sauces. The green fruits are used as vegetables and the roasted seeds resemble chestnuts in taste. The wood is hardy and of good quality.
This tree is used in tropical gardens.

BAUHINIA VARIEGATA L.

Bauhinia variegata L.
Family: *Leguminosae.*   **Common name:** ORCHID TREE.
Geographical distribution: India.   **Flowering period:** autumn thruogh spring.
Propagation: seeds and stem cutting.

Briefly deciduous tree that can grow to be up to 6 m tall. Leaves up to 12 cm in diameter, compound, pinnate, formed by two joined folioles about 2/3 of its length from the base. Flowers up to 12 cm in diameter with overlapped petals, magenta-lavender, purple or white in color with the central petals dark purple. The flowers have 5 fertile stamens and are grouped in small lateral racemes at the ends of the twigs.
Cv. candida. The white flowers have green veins. It does not require special soil or water conditions, and accepts shaded areas. It grows fast.
The bark, somewhat astringent, is used for dyes and tanning in India. The leaves and floral bottons are used as vegetables.

This tree is appropriate for small gardens to lend the touch of color, as well as for forming groups in large gardens. It is also used for lining narrow streets.

Bauhinia variegata.

BOUGAINVILLEA GLABRA

Bougainvillea glabra Choisy. 'Sanderiana'.

Common name: PAPER FLOWER. **Family:** *Nyctaginaceae.*
Flowering period: nearly year-round. **Propagation:** by cuttings.

A woody climbing plant, evergreen, inermous or with curved thorns. Leaves alternate, narrowly ovate to elliptical, acuminate, glabrous or slightly puberulent, paler beneath than above, up to 11 cm long. Flowers hermaphrodite, in clusters of three, each subtended by a purple bract, with the apex acute, undulated. Has a tubular pubescent calyx, with five lobes forming a star, acting as the corolla since it is absent; purple in colour, up to 1 cm long. Fruit in achene.
It accepts most soils and requires a sunny situation. Resistant to drought. Fast growing.
Used in gardening to cover pergolas, walls, etc.

Bougainvillea glabra 'Sanderiana'.

BOUGAINVILLEA SPECTABILIS

Bougainvillea spectabilis Willd.
Family: *Nyctaginaceae.*
Flowering period: winter-spring-early summer.

Common name: BOUGAINVILLEA.
Geographical distribution: Brazil.
Propagation: by cuttings.

A woody climber, evergreen, spiny with pubescent branches. Leaves alternate, ovate, tomentose beneath and very often also above. Up to 12 cm long. Flowers hermaphrodite in clusters of three, each subtended by a purple bract, up to 4.5 cm long. Has a tubular calyx with five lobes forming a star, acting as a corolla since it is absent, up to 2.2 cm long with abundant hair up to 1 mm long or more. Fruit in achene.
Not particular regarding soil. It requires location in bright sun. Drought resistant. Fast growing.
Used in gardening to cover walls, pergolas, banks, etc.

Bougainvillea spectabilis.

BOUGAINVILLEA SPECTABILIS CV LATERITIA

Bougainvillea spectabilis Willd. Cv. Lateritia.
Common name: BOUGAINVILLEA.
Flowering period: autumn-winter-spring-early summer.

Family: *Nyctaginaceae.*
Propagation: by cuttings.

A woody climber, evergreen, spiny, with pubescent branches. Leaves alternate, ovate, tomentose beneath and very often also above. Up to 12 cm long. Flowers hermaphrodite in clusters of three, each subtended by a brick red bract up to 5.5 cm long. Has a tubular calyx, star-shaped, five lobed, acting as a corolla since it is absent, up to 2.5 cm long, with abundant hair up to 1 mm long or more. Fruit in achene.
Not particular as far as soil. It needs to be located in bright sun. Needs little water. Fast growing.
Used in gardening to cover pergolas, walls, banks, etc.

Bougainvillea spectabilis Cv. Lateritia.

BOUGAINVILLEA X BUTTIANA

Bougainvillea X buttiana **Holtt. et Standl.** *'Mrs. Butt'.*
Common name: BOUGAINVILLEA.   **Family:** *Nyctaginaceae.*
Flowering period: nearly year-round.   **Propagation:** by cuttings.

A woody climbing plant, evergreen and spiny. Leaves alternate, broadly ovate, acuminate, glabrous, paler beneath than above, up to 20 cm long. Flowers hermaphrodite in clusters of three, each subtended by a scarlet bract; obtuse, apiculate, undulated. Calyx tubular, pubescent, five-lobed, star-shaped, acting as the corolla since it is absent. Up to 1 cm long. Fruit in achene.

It accepts most soils and needs a sunny location. Resistant to drought. Fast growing.

Used in gardening to cover pergolas, walls, taluses, etc.

Bougainvillea X buttiana 'Mrs. Butt'.

BRACHYCHITON ACERIFOLIUM

Brachychiton acerifolium (A. Cunn.) F. J. Muell. [*Sterculia acerifolia* A. Cunn.].
Family: *Sterculiaceae*.
Common name: FLAME TREE.
Geographical distribution: Australia.
Flowering period: spring-summer-autumn.
Propagation: seeds.

Brachychiton acerifolium.

Deciduous tree, up to 30 m tall. Large, 3-5-7 lobed leaves, sometimes entire. Petioles up to 70 cm long. Blades up to 27 cm long. Bell-shaped scarlet flowers, 2 cm in diameter and clustered in panicles. Fruit in blackish follicles up to 10 cm long with long peduncles. The seeds are yellow.

This tree adapts well to most kinds of soils and situations as long as it has abundant water. It grows fast. Flowering takes place when the leaves have fallen and it is very spectacular, for then the tree resembles a torch. This tree is used to line streets and avenues and is seen in most gardens and parks. When young it can be used as an indoors plant.

BRACHYCHITON DISCOLOR

Brachychiton discolor F. J. Muell. [*Sterculia discolor* (F. J. Muell.) F. J. Muell. ex Benth.].
Family: *Sterculiaceae*.
Geographical distribution: Australia.
Flowering period: spring-summer.
Propagation: seeds.

Deciduous tree seen towering up to 30 m tall. 3-5-7 lobed, angular leaves with a whitish tomentum beneath. Petioles that can be 17 cm long. Blades 30 cm long and 25 cm wide. Flowers grouped in recemes,

Brachychiton discolor.

without petals and with a pink or light red calyx, tomentose, bell-shaped and reaching lengths of up to 5 cm. Fruits in follicles up to 15 cm long, with rust colored pubescence.

This tree grows on most soils, though it prefers sunny areas. It grows fast.

It is used in gardens and parks as well as for aligning purposes.

Brachychiton discolor.

BRACHYCHITON POPULNEUM

Brachychiton populneum (Schott et Endl.) R. Br.
[B. *diversifolius* Hort., not. R. Br.; *Sterculia diversifolia* G. Don.].
Family: *Sterculiaceae.*   **Common name:** KURRAJONG.
Geographical distribution: Australia.   **Propagation:** seeds.
Flowering period: later winter-spring-summer-autumn.

Brachychiton populneum.

This evergreen tree can be seen reaching heights of up to 20 m high. Ovate or ovate-lanceolate leaves, entire or lobed, with 3-5 lobes. Petioles up to 7 cm long. Blades up to 15 cm long. White, yellowish-greenish flowers up to 1 cm in diameter. Fruits in follicle, blackish and up to 7 cm long. Yellow seeds.

This tree adapts to most soils and withstands low temperatures. It can survive droughts. In Australia its foliage is used as cattle fodder.

It is used to line city streets and avenues as well as a shade tree in gardens. When young it can be used as an indoor plant.

17

Brahea armata.

BRAHEA ARMATA

Brahea armata S. Wats. *[Erythea armata (S. Wats.) S. Wats.].*
Common name: BLUE FAN PALM.　　　　**Family:** *Palmae.*
Geographical distribution: Lower California.　　**Propagation:** by seeds.

Hermaphroditic Palm, thick trunk, up to 12 m high or more. Leaves palmate, blue, up to 2.60 m long, deeply divided in about 60 segments bipartite, slightly filiferous. Petioles with spiny margins. Inflorescence longer than leaves, about 4.5 m long or more, with pendulous branches. Flowers in clusters of three. Fruit globose, flat on one side, about 2.5 cm long, yellow.
Accepts most soils. Needs sunny location. Very slow growing. Dry leaves remain on trunk for some time.
In gardening, used individually or in groups.

18

Brassaia actinophylla.

BRASSAIA ACTINOPHYLLA

Brassaia actinophylla Endl. [*Schefflera actynophylla* (Endl.) Harms.].
Common name: AUSTRALIAN UMBRELLA TREE.   **Family:** *Araliaceae.*
Geographical distribution: Australia.   **Flowering period:** end summer-autumn.
Propagation: by seeds, cutting, shoot and air layering.

Evergreen tree up to 12 m high, often with several trunks. Leaves composite, digitate. Petioles up to 75 cm long. Folioles oblong, glossy, up to 60 cm long, growing from apex of petiole. Small flowers, red, grouped in umbels arranged in racemes up to 1 cm long. Fruit in drupe, red-purple in colour.

Prefers good quality soils. Needs sunny location, although it accepts partial shade. Fast growing.

In gardening used individually or in groups. Also as potted plant for interior decoration and patios.

BREYNIA DISTICHA

Breynia disticha J.R. Forst. et G. Forst. *[B. nivosa* (W. G. Sm.) Small].

Common name: SNOWBUSH.

Family: *Euphorbiaceae.*

Geographical distribution: Pacific Islands.

Propagation: by cutting and shoots.

Breynia disticha Cv. Roseo-Picta.

Monoecious, evergreen shrub, up to 2 m high. Leaves alternate, simple, entire, elliptical to ovate or obovate, slightly distichous, up to 5 cm long, green and white. Flowers unisexual, small, dull. Females bell-shaped, reddish. Fruits in berries. Cv. Roseo-Picta. Variegated leaves of green, white, pink and red Not demanding about soil. Accepts shade, but in strong sun it takes on more attractive colouring. Somewhat slow growing. Used in gardening individually, in groups and for hedges. Also as potted plant.

Brugmansia sanguinea.

BRUGMANSIA SANGUINEA

Brugmansia sanguinea (Ruiz et Pavón) D. Don. *[Datura sanguinea* Ruiz et Pavón].
Family: *Solanaceae.*
Geographical distribution: The Andes, from.Colombia to Chile.
Flowering period: nearly year-round   **Propagation:** by seed and cutting.

Shrub or small tree, evergreen, normally up to 3.5 m high, with young branches pubescent. Leaves alternate, ovate-oblong, coarsely dentate, pubescent, with beneath paler than above, acute, up to 25 cm long. Petioles long, pubescent. Flowers hermaphrodite, pendulous, funnel-shaped. Calyx with 1-4 teeth. Corolla red in colour with some yellow at the mouth, then changing to yellow and yellowish-green towards the base of the tube, up to 18 cm long, with five curved teeth. Fruits in berries. Accepts most soils. Tolerates completely sunny location and also shade. Needs good fertilizing and watering for good growth. Needs pruning into shape. Fast growing.
The presence of alkaloids makes all parts of the plant poisonous if eaten in large quantity. In small doses they have narcotic effects.
Used in gardening individually or in groups.

BRUGMANSIA VERSICOLOR

Brugmansia versicolor Lagerh. *[Datura mollis* Saff.].
Family: *Solanaceae.*
Flowering period: almost all year.
Geographical distribution: Ecuador.
Propagation: by seed and cutting.

Brugmansia versicolor.

Evergreen small tree up to 4.5 m high. Leaves alternate, oblong-elliptical, glabrous to pubescent, acuminate, with lengthwise petioles, up to 60 cm long. Flowers hermaphrodite, large, pendulous, funnel-shaped. Spathe-like calyx, up to 17 cm long, with one sole tooth ending in a long tip.
Corolla 5-toothed, funnel-shaped, up to 30 cm long wiht long, curved teeth; it changes colour from a salmon-tinged white at the beginning to a peach colour at the end. Fruits in berries, fusiform, up to 21 cm long.
Tolerates most soils. Lives in strong sun as well as in shade. Needs appropriate fertilizing and watering for good growth. Must be pruned into shape. Fast growing.
All parts of the plant are poisonous if eaten in large quantities; however, in small doses they have narcotic effects due to their alkaloid contents.
Used in gardening individually or in groups.

BRUGMANSIA X CANDIDA

Brugmansia X candida Pers. *[Datura X candida* (Pers.) Saff.; *B. aurea X B. versicolor].*
Family: *Solanaceae.*
Geographical distribution: Ecuador.
Propagation: by seed and cutting.
Common name: ANGEL'S TRUMPET.
Flowering period: almost year-round.

Evergreen shrub or small tree up to 6 m high. Leaves alternate, ovate to oblong-elliptical, acuminate, entire to coarsely dentate, slightly pubescent, up to 55 cm long, with lengthwise petioles. Flowers large, pendulous,

Brugmansia X candida.

white, rarely yellow or pink. Spathe-like calyx, up to 12 cm long, with only one tooth ending in prolonged tip. Corolla funnel-shaped, 5-toothed, up to 27 cm long. Teeth curved, long. Fruits in berries oblong-cilindric to fusiform, up to 18 cm long.

Not demanding about soil. Can live both in sun and shade. Needs appropriate fertilizing and watering for good growth. Needs pruning into shape. Fast growing.

All parts of the plant are poisonous if eaten in large quantity. In small doses they produce narcotic effects due to presence of alkaloids.

Used in gardening individually or in groups.

Brugmansia X candida.
Flowers.

BRUGMANSIA X INSIGNIS

Brugmansia X insignis (Barb. Rodr.) Lockw. *[B. suaveolens X B. versicolor].*
Family: *Solanaceae.*
Flowering period: autumn to spring.

Geographical distribution: Peruvian Andes.
Propagation: by seed and cutting.

Brugmansia X insignis.

Shrub or small tree, evergreen up to 4.5 m high. Leaves alternate, ovate or narrowly elliptical, acute to acuminate, entire or sinuate, pubescent up to 30 cm long, with lengthwise petioles. Flowers hermaphrodite, semipendulous. Corolla white, up to 28 cm long. 5-toothed, with curved teeth, longer than those of B. suaveolens. Anthers connivent or diverging. Fruits in berries, fusiform.

Takes to most soils. Can live in strong sun as well as in shade. Needs appropriate fertilizer and watering for good growth. Must be pruned to give it shape. Fast growing.

Contains alkaloids with strong narcotic effects, thus consumption of any part of the plant, in some amount, has mortal consequences.

Used in gardening to form groups or individually.

CAESALPINIA GILLIESII

Caesalpinia gilliesii (Wallich ex Hook.) Benth. *[Poinciana gilliesii* Wallich ex Hook.].
Family: Leguminosae.
Common name: BIRD OF PARADISE.
Geographical distribution: Argentina, Uruguay.
Flowering period: spring through autumn.
Propagación: seeds.

Deciduous shrub or small tree that can grow to be up to 6 m tall, with pubescent, glandular twigs. Bipinnate leaves up to 20 cm long. Oblong folioles up to 8 m long. Flowers in racemes growing at ends of twigs. Yellow petals up to 3 cm long; red stamens up to 9 cm long. Fruit in pods up to 10 cm long.

It grows well on most soils though it prefers sunny, rather dry areas. It grows fast. This shrub is used in tropical and subtropical gardens, either solitary or in groups.

Caesalpinia gilliesii.

CAESALPINIA PULCHERRIMA

Caesalpinia pulcherrima (L.) Swartz. *[Poinciana pulcherrima* L.].
Family: Leguminosae.
Geographical distribution: The West Indies.
Flowering period: summer through winter.

Common name: BARBADOS PRIDE.

Propagation: seeds.

Deciduous shrub or small tree up to 6 m tall, aculeate and glabrous. Bipinnate leaves, with 3-9 pairs of folioles, oblong or oblong-spatulate in shape, up to 1.5 cm long. Flowers grouped in terminal clusters. Red petals with yellow edges. Red stamens up to 6.5 cm long. The petals are occasionally yellow or pink. Fruit in oblong-linear pods, up to 12 cm long. It can grow on most soils although it favors dry, sunny areas.

Caesalpinia pulcherrima.

It grows fast. This tree is widely used in the tropics and subtropics for its beauty. It is used alone or in groups. It is also cultivated as free-growing hedges in dry areas.

Calliandra haematocephala.

CALLIANDRA HAEMATOCEPHALA

Calliandra haematocephala Hassk.
Family: *Leguminosae.*
Flowering period: autumn-winter-summer.

Geographical distribution: Bolivia.
Propagation: by seed and cutting.

Shrub or small tree, evergreen up to 4.5 m high or more. Leaves alternate, bipinnate, with two pinnas. Folioles obliquely oblong-lanceolate up to 4 cm long. Flowers hermaphrodite or functionally male in globose heads up to 7 cm in diameter. Corolla reddish. Stamen very long, with red filaments. Fruits in legumes, linear-oblanceolate.

Accepts most soils although it prefers rich, well drained ones. Needs sunny location. Moderate growth.

Used in gardening individually or in groups.

Carica papaya.

CARICA PAPAYA

Carica papaya L.
Family: Caricaceae.
Propagation: seeds.

Common name: PAPAW.
Geographical distribution: Tropical America.

Semiwoody tree with an average height of 3-6 m. The palmeate-lobed leaves can reach 60 cm in diameter. There are male, female and hermaphrodite plants. Yellow female flowers 3.5-5 cm long growing alone or in small racemes up to 7.5 cm long. Male, white-creamish or yellow flowers up to 2.5 cm long, growing in pendulous panicles, 27-75 cm long. The hermaphrodite flowers are divided into three types: elongate, pentandriate and intermediate. Male and hermaphrodite can also produce female flowers. The fruits resemble cantaloupes, with yellow or orange-reddish pulp.

Papaws prefer loam, rich and well-drained soils, with plenty of sun. It dies in stagnant water. Fast growing. Fairly drought resistant.

It is cultivated for its fruit which is eaten fresh from the tree; the fruit is also very good for the digestion owing to the papain, an alkaloid widely used in pharmaceutics. Shades, sweets, jellies and other delicacies are made with it. Gardens acquire a tropical touch with this tree.

CARISSA MACROCARPA

Carissa macrocarpa (Eckl.) A.DC. *[C. grandiflora* (E.H. Mey.) A.DC.]
Family: *Apocynaceae.*
Geographical distribution: South Africa.
Propagation: by seed, cutting and air layering.

Common name: NATAL PLUM.
Flowering period: nearly year-round.

Carissa macrocarpa.

Evergreen shrub, up to 4 m high, very ramified, spiny. Leaves opposite, broadly ovate, coriaceous, mucronate, dark green above and paler underneath, up to 10 cm long. Flowers hermaphrodite, clustered in terminal cymes with few flowers, sometimes one sole flower. Corolla salverform, up to 6 cm in diameter, white, fragant, with tube up to 1.5 cm long and lobes oblong to elliptical much longer than tube. Fruits in berries, ovoid scarlet coloured up to 5 cm long.
Prefers light, well-drained soils. Grows better in dry, sunny places. Resistent to sea mist. Slow growing.
Fruit edible fresh or used in preparing preserves and jams.
In gardening used individually or to form groups and hedges.
Recommended for coastal gardens.

CARYOTA MITIS

Caryota mitis Lour. *[C. furfuracea* Blume].
Family: *Palmae.*
Geographical distribution: Buraa to Malaysian Peninsula, Java and Philippinas.
Propagation: by seed.

Monoecious palm that usually produces several trunks, up to 3.5 m high and about 15 cm in diameter. Leaves bipinnate about 2.5 m long, with pinnules obliquely cuneate, dentate, similar to a fish tail. Inflorescences

Caryota mitis.
General aspect and detail.

branched, with pendulous
sprigs, having unisexual
flowers. The inflorescences
appear first in the upper part
of trunk and then gradually
lower until the fruit of the
lowest one ripens; then the trunk dies. Fruit globose, reddish, up to 1.5 cm
in diameter.

Needs rich soil and abundant moisture. Prefers a sunny location, accepting
some shade. Fast growing. In gardening used individually or in groups.
Also as a potted plant for decorating patios.

Caryota urens.

CARYOTA URENS

Caryota urens L.
Family: *Palmae.*
Propagation: seeds.

Common name: WINE PALM.
Geographical distribution: India, Sri Lanka and The Malay.

Monoecious palm with unbranched trunk that can reah a height of 18 m. Bipinnate leaves up to 6 m long. Pinnules resembling fish tails up to 15 cm long. Branched inflorescences with pendulous sprigs and unisexual flowers. The inflorescences appear first on the higher part of the and gradually move down until the fruit in the lower part of the tree are ripe; this is when the tree dies. Globose fruits, red purple when ripe, up to 1.5 cm in diameter. It prefers good quality, humid soils but will also tolerate less favourable spots. It grows best in sunny areas and accepts shaded regions; it is a fast-growing tree.

In India and Sri Lanka the petioles of the leaves are used to obtain a fiber to make brooms and brushes. The sap is used to make palm tree wine and sugar of good quality. The medulla produces a sort of flour or «sago» (starch).

This palm tree is widely cultivated in tropical and subtropical gardens around the world. It is recommended for growing in patios.

30

CASSIA DIDYMOBOTRYA

Cassia didymobotrya Fresen.
Family: *Leguminosae.*
Geographical distribution: Tropical Africa.
Flowering period: throughout the year.
Propagation: seeds.

CASSIA SPECTABILIS

Cassia spectabilis DC.
Family: *Leguminosae.*
Geographical distribution: Tropical America.
Flowering period: summer-autumn.
Propagation: seed and stem cutting.

Cassia didymobotrya.

Cassia spectabilis.

Evergreen shrub growing up to a height of 3 m. Pinnate leaves, up to 40 cm long. Oblong to ovate-elliptical folioles, with rounded apex, mucronate, up to 5 cm long. Flowers in upright racemes up to 30 cm long. Yellow petals and brown sepals. Fruit in pods up to 10 cm long.
It grows well on most kinds of soil, though it prefers dry, sunny areas. It grows fast.
This shrub is used in tropical and subtropical gardens owing to its beautiful flowers.

Deciduous tree sometimes reaching heights of 18 m, although in the Canary Islands it does not grow taller than 8 m. Paripinnate leaves up to 45 cm long. Ovate-lance-shaped folioles, tomentous, up to 8 cm long. Yellow flowers in terminal, upright panicles up to 60 cm long. Fruit in pods, cylindrical, up to 30 cm long, blackish in color.
This tree does not require special soils, though it needs the sun for flowering. It grows fast.
It is used in tropical and subtropical gardens for its splendid, beautiful flowers. It is also used for lining in streets, avenues and roads.

Castanospermun
australe.

CASTANOSPERMUN AUSTRALE

Castanospermun australe A. Cunn. et C. Frasser.
Family: *Leguminosae.*
Flowering period: spring-summer.

Common name: MORETOM BAY CHESNUT.
Geographical distribution: Australia.
Propagation: seeds.

Evergreen tree up to 18 m tall. Imparipinnate, dark green, glossy leaves, up to 45 cm long. Oblong leaflets up to 13 cm long. Yellow, orange to reddish flowers up to 4 cm long, grouped in lateral racemes up to 15 cm long. Fruit in pods up to 25 cm long.
It grows well in most soils and conditions, but requires sunny areas.
The seeds, resembling chestnuts, are edible and are eaten roasted.
It is utilized in parks for the beauty of its foliage, flowers and fruits. It is also used an indoor plant in flower-pots.

CESTRUM AURANTIACUM

Cestrum aurantiacum Lindl.
Family: *Solanaceae.*
Flowering period: summer-autumn.

Geographical distribution: Guatemala.
Propagación: seeds and stem cutting.

Evergreen, semiclimbing shrub or small tree growing to be up to 6 m tall. Entire, ovate-lance-shaped leaves up to 15 cm long. Sessile, yellow flowers up to 2.5 cm long grouped in axillar and terminal racemes which are in turn grouped in terminal panicles. Fruit in berries, white, up to 1.2 cm in diameter.
This species grows on most soils and requires sunny or slightly shaded areas. It is cultivated in gardens to cover walls exposed to the sun, both solitary or forming groups.

Cestrum aurantiacum.

CESTRUM NOCTURNUM

Cestrum nocturnum L.
Family: *Solanaceae.*
Flowering period: spring-summer-autumn.

Common name: NIGHT JESSAMINE.
Geographical distribution: West Indies.
Propagation: seeds and cuttings.

Cestrum nocturnum.

Evergreen shrub that can grow up to a height of 3.5 m. Ovalate-lanceolate, narrow leaves, acuminate, up to 22 cm long. Beige, or greenish white flowers, very fragrant at night, up to 2.5 cm long, clustered in axillar racemes. Berry-like fruit, white in color.

It tolerates most soils, though it requires sunny or slightly shaded areas. It is affected by droughts and requires an adequate treatment of fertilizers. It needs to be pruned regularly, for it tends to shed the lower leaves.

It is used in gardening alone or in groups to make hedges of informal type.

33

CHAMAEDOREA ELEGANS

Chamaedorea elegans Mart. [*Collinia elegans* (Mart.) Liebm. ex Ørst.].
Family: *Palmae.*　　　　　　　　**Common name:** PARLOR PALM.
Geographical distribution: Mexico Guatemala.　　**Propagation:** seeds.

Chamaedorea elegans.

Dioecious palm up to 1.80 m tall with a thin trunk, 2.5-3.5 in diameter, ringed. Pinnate, widely lanceolate leaves, up to 60-100 cm long. Linear to narrowly lanceolate pinnae, up to 20 cm long and 2.5 cm wide. Inflorescences with long peduncles. Female, pale yellow flowers. Male flowers similar to female flowers but having a pistilode instead of a pistil. Globular fruit, black, approximately 6 mm in diameter.
It prefers rich, well-drained soils. It needs shade and moist conditions.
It is widely cultivated as an indoor plant; it withstands well conditions with little light and humidity frequently found in homes. It is also used in gardens, both alone or in groups.
To obtain seeds it is necessary to plant both sexes together and do a manual pollination.

CHAMAEDOREA ERNESTI-AUGUSTI

Chamaedorea ernesti-augusti H. Wendl.
Family: *Palmae.*　　　　　　**Propagación:** seeds.
Geographical distribution: Mexico through Honduras.

Dioecious palm with a single trunk, ringed, 2 cm in diameter and with a height of approximately 1.80 m. Leaves widely cuneate-obovate, deeply bifid at the apex, with serrated edges, up to 60 cm long. Inflorescences with long peduncles, almost always standing upright. Orange, small flowers. Berries, ellipsoidal in shape, black and up to 15 mm long. Like all the Chamaedorea species it requires shady, damp areas, and it grows best in rich, well-drained soils. This is a very beautiful palm cultivated in gardens either alone or in groups. It is also used as an indoor plant.

Chamaedorea ernesti-augusti.

CHAMAEROPS HUMILIS

Chamaerops humilis L.
Common name: MEDITERRANEAN FAN PALM.
Geographical distribution: Mediterranean area.

Family: *Palmae.*
Propagation: seeds and sprouts.

Chamaerops humilis.

Dioecious or polygamous-dioecious palm, usually having a shrub-like biotype with several trunks, approximately 1.50 m tall, although at times it acquires the usual palm configuration, reaching heights of up to 6 m. Palmate, green, or often glaucus leaves. Spiny petioles. Blades 60-90 cm wide, deeply divided into segments with only one prominent vein. Very short inflorescence. Fruit variable in shape and size, edible. Its colour varies from yellow to dark orange or brown.

This palm withstands the cold very well, up to 9º C below zero. It requires sunny or slightly shady areas. It does not require special soils and its growth process is slow. The leaves are used to make brooms, hats, etc. The end bud is edible. It is used to give gardens a tropical air. It is also used to decorate patios, growing in flowerpots.

Chorisia speciosa.

CHORISIA SPECIOSA

Chorisia speciosa St. -Hil.
Family: *Bombacaceae.*
Flowerig period: autumn.

Common name: FLOSS-SILK TREE.
Geographical distribution: Brazil and Argentina.
Propagation: seeds.

Deciduous tree growing to be 15 m tall. The trunk is wide at the base, spiny and green. Compound, digitate leaves, with 5-7 lanceolate, serrated folioles, up to 12 cm long. Large, beautiful flowers up to 15 cm in diameter. White or yellowish to violet flowers on the higher parts, white or beige on the lower parts, with spots or grooves of the same color as in the higher part. Fruits in oblong capsules, pearshaped, up to 20 cm long, with a large number of seeds. It grows well on most soils as long as it has abundant water. It is somewhat cold resistant and is cultivated on the Mediterranean coast.

Inside the fruit there are hairs resembling cotton used to stuff cushions and pillows. It is used in gardens owing to its beauty.

Chrysalidocarpus lutescens.

CHRYSALIDOCARPUS LUTESCENS

Chrysalidocarpus lutescens H. Wendl. [*Areca lutescens* Bory].

Family: *Palmae.*   **Common name:** YELLOW PALM.

Geographical distribution: Madagascar.   **Propagation:** seeds and sprouts.

Monocoecious palm with several thin, ringed trunks reaching a height of up to 9 m. Pinnate leaves, 2.25 m long, gracefully arched in shape. Yellowish petiole and rachis. Branched inflorescences that appear among the flowers, accompanied by small white or yellowish flowers. Ovoid, yellow fruits, up to 2 cm long.

Although this palm tree can grow in open sunny areas, it prefers shady areas, with rich soil and abundant water. It grows fast.

It is cultivated in tropical and subtropical gardens alone and in groups as natural screens. It is also used in patios and inside homes as a decorative plant in flowerpots.

CIBOTIUM SCHIEDEI

Cibotium schiedei Schlechtend. et Cham.
Common name: MEXICAN TREE FERN.
Geographical distribution: Mexico y Guatemala.

Family: *Dicksoniaceae.*

Propagation: by spores.

Cibotium schiedei.

Tree fern up to 4.5 m high that sometimes produces sprouts at its base. Trunk and bases of the petioles covered with silky hairs yellow-brown in colour. Fronds tripinnate, oblong-deltoid, glacous beneath, gracefully arched, up to nearly 3 m long. Primary divisions oblong-lanceolate, up to 70 cm long. Secundary pinnas linear-lanceolate. Pinnules lanceolate, serrate. Sorus with bivalve indusium, valves similar in texture, but different from that of the fronds.

Needs soil rich in organic material, with good drainage. Also needs shady location. Slow growing.

Long hairs covering the cauline apex have been used as a bandage like cotton.

In gardening used as individual sample or in groups. Also as potted plant.

CLERODENDRUM SPECIOSISSIMUM

Clerodendrum speciosissimum Van Geert *[C. fallax* Lindl.].
Family: *Verbenaceae.*
Flowering period: nearly year-round.

Geographical distribution: Java.
Propagation: by seed and cuttings.

Evergreen shrub up to 3.5 m high. Branches tetragonal. Leaves opposite, cordate-ovate, thickly pubescent, entire or dentate, up to 27 cm long. Petioles long, pubescent. Flowers hermaphrodite, scarlet, up to 3.5 cm in diameter, in cymes forming erect panicles terminal up to 40 cm long. Tube of corolla up to 1.5 cm long. Stamens exserted and curved. Fruits in drupes, bluish-black in colour, with two grooves perpendicular subtended by the reddish calyx.

Accepts most soils. Needs exposure to strong sun or half shade, and plenty of water. Pruning best after flowering to prevent legginess.

Widely used in gardening for its beautiful flowering, individually as well as in groups.

Clerodendrum speciosissimum

CLIVIA MINIATA

Clivia miniata Regel.
Family: *Amaryllidaceae.*
Flowering period: spring-early summer.

Common name: KAFFIR LILY.
Geographical distribution: South Africa.
Propagation: by seed and division.

Herbaceous, perennial, acaulescent plant, with fleshy roots. Leaves perennial, arched, strap-shaped, up to 65 cm long and almost 4 cm wide, glossy, ending in a point. Flowers erect, hermaphrodite, clustered in umbels. Perianth petaloid, funnel-shaped, up to 7.5 cm long, with very short tube and lobes reddish with yellowish base. Fruits in berries, ovoid, red in colour.
Prefers rich soils, with good drainage and abundant moisture. Needs shady site.
In gardening used to form groups. Also as potted plant for decorating patios and interiors

Clivia miniata.

CLIVIA X CYRTANTHIFLORA

Clivia X cyrtanthiflora (van Houtte) Wittm. *[C.miniata X C. nobilis.]*
Family: *Amaryllidaceae.*   **Flowering period:** nearly year-round.
Propagation: by seed and division.

Clivia x cyrtanthiflora.

Herbaceous, perennial, acaulescent plant, with carnose roots. Leaves perennial, obtuse, strap-shaped canaliculate, glossy, over 90 cm long and up to 5.5 cm wide. Flowers hermaphrodite, pendulous, grouped in umbels. Perianth petaloid, curved, funnel-shaped, up to 4.5 cm long and 3.2 cm in diameter, with short tube and lobes with reddish and yellowish tones. Fruits in berries.
Prefers rich soils, with good drainage and plenty of moisture. Needs a shady location.
Used in gardening to form groups. Also as potted plant.

COCCOLOBA UVIFERA

Coccoloba uvifera (L.) L.   **Family:** *L. Polygonaceae.*
Common name: SEA GRAPE.   **G. distribution:** Antilles and Tropical America.
Flowering period: spring-summer.   **Propagation:** seeds.

Evergreen that usually grows to be 6 m tall, though occasionally it can be seen reaching 12 m. Large leaves, up to 25 cm wide, circular to reniform, glossy, leathery, with prominent red veins. Small, white flowers, very fragrant and growing in racemes up to 30 cm long. Subglobular fruit purple when ripe, up to 2 cm in diameter, grouped in racemes resembling grape bunches. It can grow on poor quality soils and withstands drought, the wind and sea mist.

Coccoloba uvifera.

The fruit is edible and the wood is used in carpentry. This tree is recommended for coastal gardens, and is used to line streets and in public parks.

Coccoloba uvifera. Detail.

Cocos nucifera.

COCOS NUCIFERA

Cocos nucifera L.
Family: *Palmae.*
Propagation: seeds.

Common name: COCONUT PALM.
Geographical distribution: Tropical Melanesia.

Monocoecious palm with ringed trunk, normally somewhat curved and with a wide base. Pinnate leaves 5-7 cm long. Pinnas 90 cm long, green-yellowish in color. Branched inflorescences. White flowers, the female ones up to 2.5 cm in diameter and the male slightly smaller. Large fruits, green-yellowish, with a fibrous mesocarp and containing one seed.

The coconut palm grows well in warm, humid areas, preferably near the coast. It prefers sandy soil. Slow growing in subtropical areas. It withstands coastal salinity, but is affected by the cold.

This is the most useful palm tree in the world. From its dried endosperm (copra) is obtained coconut oil. The fibers of the mesocarp are used to make rugs, ropes, etc. Sugar and alcohol are made from its sap. The endosperm of the seeds is eaten directly from the fruit. Its milky juice is both drunk as a refreshment and used in cooking.

This species is very common in tropical and subtropical gardens, especially those located along the coast. It is usually cultivated in groups. The first leaves of sprouting coconuts are also now being used as an indoor plant.

CODIAEUM VARIEGATUM

Codiaeum variegatum Blume var. *pictum* Muell. Arg. [*Croton pictum*. Lodd.].
Family: *Euphorbiaceae.*
Common name: CROTON.   **Propagation:** usually by stem cutting.
Geographical distribution: The Moluca Islands.and Malaysia.

Codiaeum variegatum.

Evergreen shrub growing to be up to 3.5 m tall. Leathery leaves, with different shapes, sizes and colors. Unisexual flowers, growing in terminal, axillary racemes. It grows well on most soils as long as they are well drained. The shrubs cultivated in open, sunny areas acquire a greater variety of colors than those growing in the shade. The perfect place for these plants to grow is semishady areas. They need plenty of water. In the Pacific Islands the natives use the leaves to make some of their clothes. In the Malay Paninsula this plant is used for medicinal purposes. It is widely used in tropical and subtropical gardens and is very popular as an indoor plant. There are many cultivars.

COLLETIA CRUCIATA

Colletia cruciata Hook.
Family: *Rhamnaceae.*
Common name: ANCHOR PLANT.
Geographical distribution: South of Brazil and Uruguay.
Flowering period: nearly year-round.
Propagation: by seed and cuttings.

Colletia Cruciata.

Deciduous shrub up to 3 m high. Branches with triangular thorns up to 5 cm long, flat which are actually modified sprigs ending in very sharp point. Each pair of thorns is arranged in a right angle to the pairs immediately before and after it. Leaves ovate, small, usually absent. Flowers hermaphrodite, small, yellowish-white, apetalous, tubular, solitary or forming groups at the base of the thorns. Fruit capsuled.
Little demanding regarding soil, as long as it is well drained. Needs a sunny location. Slow growing. Drought resistant.
Used in gardening alone or in groups.

44

Coprosma repens.

Evergreen shrub or small tree up to 7.5 m tall. Thick, ovate or oblong leaves, shiny green above, dull green beneath, up to 11 cm long. The fruit is a drupe, obovoid, yellow-orange, up to 9 mm long, grouped in racemes. The natural habitat of this species is rocky areas where it does not grow taller than 90 cm. It can grow in the shade or in the open and withstands the proximity of the ocean.
It is used in gardening for making hedges, groups and as a solitary plant.

Evergreen tree growing to be 10-12 m tall. Ensiform leaves up to 90 cm long and 6 cm wide, that grow at the ends of the branches in clusters. Small, white, fragrant flowers growing in terminal panicles. Berry-like fruit, whitish, globular, up to 6 mm in diameter.
It does not require special soils and can grow both in the sun and in the shade. It grows slowly.
A very strong fiber is obtained from its leaves.
It is used for indoor decoration and in gardens.

Cordyline australis.

CORYNOCARPUS LAEVIGATA

Corynocarpus laevigata J. R. Forst. et G. Forst.
Family: *Corynocarpaceae.*
Geographical distribution: New Zealand.
Propagation: seeds.

Common name: NEW ZEALAND LAUREL.
Flowering period: spring.

Evergreen tree up to 12 m tall. Elliptical-oblong to oblong-obovate leaves, shiny green, up to 18 cm long. Small, greenish or whitish flowers growing in terminal panicles up to 20 cm long. Fruit in drupes, orange in color and fragrant, up to 4 cm long.

It accepts most soils, but prefers sunny areas. It withstands the proximity of the ocean. The fruit, similar to the medlar, hence its name «fragrant medlar», is edible. The seeds are poisonous.

This is a very ornamental plant, used to line streets as well as in gardens in general. Its shape resembles the magnolia plant.

Corynocarpus laevigata.

CRESCENTIA CUJETE

Crescentia cujete L.
Common name: CALABASH TREE GÜIRA.
Family: *Bignoniaceae.*
Geographical distribution: Tropical America
Flowering period: autumn.
Propagation: seeds and stem cutting.

Evergreen or slightly deciduous tree reaching up to 12 m in height. Oblong or oblanceolate leaves up to 24 cm long. Large foetid-smelling flowers up to 10 cm long, greenwhitish with purple veins and spots; they grow on the trunk or branches. Fruit up to 40 cm in diameter, globose or oviform, yellow-greenish in color.
It does not require special soils, though it prefers sunny areas. It grows fast and accepts the proximity of the sea. It withstands droughts.
When the pulp and seeds are removed from the fruit, it is used as container, or to make maracas or smoking pipes, owing to the woody mesocarp.
This tree is cultivated in public and private gardens, alone and in groups.

Crescentia cujete.

CRINUM MOOREI

Crinum moorei Hook.
Family: *Amaryllidaceae.*
Flowering period: spring-summer.

Geographical distribution: South Africa.
Propagation: by seed and division.

Crinum Moorei.

Perennial, herbaceous plant, with thick tunicate bulbs, having a long neck up to 65 cm long. Leaves ensiform, canaliculate, entire, arched, up to 125 cm long and 15 cm wide. Flowers hermaphrodite, clustered in umbel at end of floral scape up to 150 cm long. Perianth petaloid, funnel-shaped, up to 20 cm in diameter or more, with tepals oblong, acute, white with rosaceous tones. Curved tube up to 12 cm long, green. Fruit capsuled. Needs rich soil with good drainage and plenty of moisture. Can live in strong sun as well as in shade, although it prefers partial shade.

Used in gardening in groups. Also as a potted plant.

CRINUM PEDUNCULATUM

Crinum pedunculatum R.Br.
Family: *Amaryllidaceae.*
Flowering period: spring-summer.

Geographical distribution: Australia.
Propagation: by seed and division.

Crinum pedunculatum.

Perennial, herbaceous plant, with tunicate bulbs, having a thick neck up to 45 cm long. Leaves perennial, ensiform, canaliculate, up to 160 cm long and 14 cm wide. Flowers hermaphrodite, clustered in umbel at the end of a floral scape up to 120 cm long. Perianth petaloid, salverform, up to 17 cm in diameter with tepals linear, white in colour. Tube straight or somewhat curved up to 8 cm long, green. Fruit capsuled.

Needs rich soil with abundant moisture and good drainage. Prefers strong sun or partial shade.

Used in gardening in groups. Also as a potted plant.

CRYPTOSTEGIA MADAGASCARIENSIS

Cryptostegia madagascariensis Bojer.
Family: *Asclepiadaceae.*
Geographical distribution: Madagascar.
Propagation: by seed and cuttings.

Common name: PURPLE ALAMANDA.
Flowering period: late spring-summer-autumn.

Evergreen, woody, climbing plant. Leaves simple, opposite, somewhat revolute, glabrous, oblong, acuminate, dark green in colour and glossy above and paler beneath, up to 10 cm long. Hermaphrodite flowers grouped in terminal cymes. Corolla funnel-shaped, five-lobed, purple, up to 5.5 cm in diameter. Crown with entire lobes. Fruits in follicles, in pairs, greenish, up to 10 cm long.
Accepts most soils. Needs a sunny site. After pruning it has a shrubbish appearance. Somewhat slow growing.
Used in gardening to cover pergolas, walls, etc.

Cryptostegia madagascariensis.

CUPHEA IGNEA

Cuphea ignea A. DC. *[C. platycentra* Lem., not Benth.].
Family: *Lythraceae.*
Geographical distribution: Mexico and Jamaica.
Propagation: by seed and cuttings.

Common name: CIGAR FLOWER.
Flowering period: nearly year-round.

Evergrenn shrub up to 90 cm high. Leaves opposite, oblong to lanceolate, up to 4 cm long or more. Flowers hermaphrodite, tubulose, apetalous, axillary. Calyx up to 2.5 cm long, with scarlet-coloured tube and violet limb with white segment. Fruits in capsules.
Not demanding regarding soil. Thrives in strong sun as well as in shade.
Needs plenty of water. Slow growing.
Flowers look like small lit cigars.
Used in gardening individually or in groups.

Cuphea ignea.

CYCAS REVOLUTA

Cycas revoluta Thunb.
Family: *Cycadaceae.*
Propagation: seeds and sprouts.

Common name: SAGO PALM.
Geographical distribution: Japan.

Dioecious plant 2-3 m tall. Erect trunk, topped with a crown of pinnate leaves up to 110 cm long, that give it its palm tree aspect. The folioles are linear-lanceolate, up to 16 cm long, with acute tips and revolute edges. The male inflorescences are shaped as terminal cones and are 40-50 cm long; the female ones consist of a bunch of carpelled, whitish, extended leaves that start at the apex of the trunk. The ovules are located on its edges. The red, oval seeds are over 4 cm long. This plant prefers rich soils with adequate draining. It can live in the sun but grows better in semishaded areas. It grows slowly.

From the medulla of the trunk is obtained a kind of flour known as «sago» that has become less used because it has carcinogenic properties.

This tree is widely used indoors and in gardens. It is ideal for inside courtyards, and is seen in bonsais.

Cycas revoluta.

DELONIX REGIA

Delonix regia (Bojer) Raf. [*Poinciana regia* Bojer].   **Common name:** FLAME OF THE FOREST.
Family: *Leguminosae.*   **Geographical distribution:** Madagascar.
Flowering period: spring-summer.   **Propagation:** seeds.

Deciduous tree reaching to 10-12 m tall, with umbrella-like horizontal branches. Oval, bipinnate leaves up to 40 cm long. Pinnae up to 10 cm long. Oblong folioles, approximately 1 cm long. Dark red to orange-red flowers up to 12 cm in diameter, grouped in corymbiform racemes. The higher petal is white in trees with dark red flowers, and it is yellow in those with red-orange flowers. Fruit in pods up to 60 cm long and 5 cm or more wide. It accepts most soils as long as they are well drained. It requires sun and does not withstand the wind well. It has a very agressive root system; for this reason it must not be planted near buildings. It can grow near the sea and its growth process is fast.
Its bark has medicinal properties and the seeds are used to make necklaces.
This is one of the most beautiful flower trees seen in tropical regions. It is cultivated in parks, private gardens and in avenues.

Delonix regia.

DICTYOSPERMA ALBUM

Dictyosperma algum (Bory) H. Wendl. et Drude ex Scheff. *[D. rubrum* Nichols.].
Family: *Palmae.*   **Common name:** PRINCESS PALM.
Geographical distribution: Mascarene Islands.**Propagation:** by seeds.

Monoecious palm with grayish trunk, annulate, up to 14 m high or more. Leaves pinnate up to 3.60 m long. Shells of leaves form a crownshaft. Pinnas linear-lanceolate, acuminate, up to 60 cm long, with veins well marked. Inflorescence in lower part of culm, up to 40 cm long. Flowers in triads, two male and one female. Fruit ellipsoidal, up to 2 cm long, purple. Prefers rich, well-drained soils. Needs sunny location. Fast growing. In gardening used individually or in groups. Also as potted plant for interior decoration.

Dictyosperma Album.

DISTICTIS BUCCINATORIA

Distictis buccinatoria (DC.) A. Gentry *[Phaedranthus buccinatorius* (DC.) Miers].
Family: *Bignoniaceae.*　　　　　　　　**Geographical distribution:** Mexico.
Flowering period: nearly all year.　　　**Propagation:** by cuttings and air layering..

Woody climbing plant, evergreen. Quadrangular branches. Leaves
opposite made up of two folioles and a terminal tendril. Folioles elliptical
to obovate-oblong, acuminate, up to 11 cm long. Flowers hermaphrodite
clustered in terminal racemes pendulous, with few flowers. Corolla tubular
funnel-shaped, up to 8 cm long, five-lobed, with yellowish tubes with
reddish tones and the limb blood red or purple-red. Stamens exserted.
Fruits in capsules.
Not particular about soil, as long as it is well-drained. Needs sunny site.
Fast growing. Prefers abundant watering.
Used to cover walls, pergolas, etc.

Distictis buccinatoria

DOMBEYA X CAYEUXII

Dombeya X cayeuxii André. *[D. bourgessiae X D. wallichii].*
Family: *Sterculiaceae.*   **Flowering period:** autumn-winter.
Propagation: stem cutting.

Evergreen shrub or small tree reaching a height of up to 7 m tall.
Alternate, heart-shaped, serrated leaves, sometimes longer than 30 cm,
covered with hairs. Pink flowers, grouped in pendular umbels and
provided with long peduncles. Pubescent bracts in the umbel, up to 2.5 cm
long and 1.25 cm wide. Fruits in capsules.
This plant can grow on poor soils and tolerates drought, but it grows best
in favorable conditions. It withstands the shade but prefers the sun.
It is very used in gardens, alone and forming groups.

Dombeya X cayeuxii.

DURANTA REPENS

Duranta repens. L. *[D. plumieri* Jacq.].
Family: *Verbenaceae.*   **Geographical distribution:** Florida to Brazil.
Flowering period: nearly year-round.   **Propagation:** by seed and cuttings.

Duranta repens.

53

Shrub or small tree up to 5.5 m high, occasionally spiny, with branches gracefully arched. Leaves simple, opposite or verticillate, ovate to obovate, entire or coarsely dentate in upper part, up to 13.5 cm long. Flowers hermaphrodite, grouped in panicles. Corolla salverform, five-lobed, lilac in colour, up to 12 mm in diameter. Fruits in drupes, yellow, approx. 1 cm in diameter.

Accepts most soils. Resists drought, but grows better with plenty of water. Prefers a sunny location, although allows partial shade. Fast growing. Should be pruned after fruit falls in order to obtain better flowering. Used in gardening individually, in groups or as hedge.

Duranta repens. Detalil.

ERYTHRINA CAFFRA

Erythrina caffra Thunb.
Family: *Leguminosae.*
Geographical distribution: South Africa.
Propagation: by seed and cuttings.

Common name: ERYTHANA, COAST KAFFIRBOOM.
Flowering period: winter-early spring.

Deciduous tree up to 20 m high, with trunk and branches spiny. Leaves alternate, imparipinnate, with lengthwise petioles. Folioles in threes (sometimes fives), rhomboidal-ovate, acuminate, the central one larger than side ones, up to 16 cm wide. Flowers hermaphrodite, red-orange in colour (sometimes cream-coloured), clustered on racemes. Standard strongly reflex, up to 6 cm long and 4 cm wide, not enclosing other parts of the flower. Fruits in legumes, constricting, curved, up to 20 cm long. Seeds red, glossy, with dark-coloured hilum.

Tolerates most soils. Prefers sunny location. Resistant to droughts and frost. Fast growing.

The flowering of this tree, which begins when leafless, used to indicate to the Bantu that it was time to sow their crops. The seeds, poisonous, are used by the native women to make necklaces as they are thought to bring good luck. The wood is used to make canoes.

In gardening it is used as a shade tree in parks and gardens and to line city streets.

Erythrina caffra.

ERYTHRINA CRISTA-GALLI

Erythrina crista-galli L.
Family: *Leguminosae.*
Flowering period: spring-summer-autumn.
Geographical distribution: Brazil, Argentina,Uruguay and Paraguay.

Common name: COCKSPUR CORAL TREE.
Propagation: seeds.

Deciduous tree growing to be up to 8 m tall, althoug it is sometimes a shrub. Spiny branches and petioles. Trifoliate leaves up to 28 cm long. Lanceolate or ovate-lanceolate folioles, the terminal foliole being the largest, up to 16 cm long. Red, cockscombed flowers up to 5 cm long, grouped in dense racemes up to 50 cm long. Fruit in pods, brown, up to 30 cm long.

It prefers light, well-drained soils. It needs abundant water in the spring and summer. Fairly cold resistant. In Argentina it is known as «seibo» and its flower is the «national flower».The bark is used as a medicine. The wood is used for making rafts, cart wheels, etc.

Owing to its beautiful flowers it is cultivated in gardens.

Erythrina crista-galli.

EUCALYPTUS FICIFOLIA

Eucalyptus ficifolia F. J. Muell.
Family: *Myrtaceae.*
Common name: RED-FLOWERING GUM.
Propagation: seeds.

Geographical distribution: Australia.
Flowering period: spring-summer-autumn.

Evergreen tree growing to a height of to 9 m. Ovate-lanceolate leaves up to 15 cm long. Flowers in umbels grouped in panicles, in colors that range from white and pink to orange and red. The lobes of the calyx and the petals are joined to form a calyptra. Fruit in capsules, woody, urn-shaped, up to 3.2 cm in diameter and 4.5 long.

It prefers heavy, hardy soil and grows badly in sandy areas. It withstands cold, heat and drought and requires a sunny spot to grow.

It is a very spectacular tree when its flowers blossom. It is used to line streets as well as in parks and gardens.

Eucalyptus ficifolia.

EUGENIA UNIFLORA

Eugenia uniflora L.
Geographical distribution: Tropical America.
Flowering period: several times throughout the year.

Family: *Myrtaceae.*
Common name: SURINAM CHERRY.
Propagation: seeds.

Eugenia uniflora.

Eugenia uniflora.
Detail.

Evergreen shrub or small tree up to 6 m tall. Opposite, ovate-lanceolate leaves up to 6 cm long, provided with short petioles, dark green above, paler beneath. Solitary white flowers, about 1.5 cm in diameter, growing on long peduncles. Globose-ovoid fruits, red when ripe and with eight longitudinal grooves.

This tree grows well on most soils although it does best in rich, well-drained terrain, preferring a slightly shady spot. It grows fast and requires adequate watering and fertilizing. It is widely cultivated in tropical regions. The edible fruit is used to make jam, jelly and sherbets.

In gardening it is used alone or for making hedges, as it can be pruned. It can also grow in flowerpots.

EUPHORBIA PULCHERRIMA

Euphorbia pulcherrima Willd. ex Klotzsch.
[*Poinsettia pulcherrima* (Willd. ex Klotzsch.) R. C. Grah.].
Family: *Euphorbiaceae.*
Geographical distribution: Mexico and Central America.
Common name: POINSETTIA.
Flowering period: autumn-winter.
Propagation: stem cutting.

Deciduous shrub up to 4 m tall. Ovate-ellyptical to lanceolate or panduriform leaves, dentate or lobed, up to 32 cm long. Very small flowers clustered in cyathia. The cyathia are grouped in terminal cymes, resembling umbels, surrounded by lanceolate bracts, as large as the leaves, red in color. This is a hardy, shrub that grows on most soils, though it prefers sunny areas. To obtain better flowers they must be pruned soon after flowering. It grows fast.
It is widely cultivated and there are cultivars with bracts with different tones of red, white and pink.
It is used as a garden shrub, on roadsides, as flower in bunches, in flowerpots and especially at Christmas.

Euphorbia pulcherrima.

FEIJOA SELLOWIANA

Feijoa sellowiana O. Berg.
Common name: PINEAPPLE GUAVA.
Family: *Myrtaceae.*
Geographical distribution: Southern de Brazil, Uruguay, Paraguay y Argentina.
Fruiting period: autumn.
Propagation: seeds, stem cutting and air layering.

Feijoa sellowiana.

Evergreen shrub or small tree up to 6 m tall with white-tomentous branches. Ellyptical-oblong, opposite leaves, dark green above, white-tomentous beneath, up to 7.5 cm long. Hermaphrodite flowers, solitary, 3 cm in diameter, with fleshy petals, purple inside and white-tomentous outside. Red stamen. Fruit in berries, oval or oblong, green and coated with a fine, whitish dust, 5 to 7.5 cm long. It grows well in subtropical, dry regions, with cool weather a part of the year. It prefers loam, rich in organic matter. It withstands drought and although it accepts some shade it thrives in the sun.

It is grow for its edible, fruit that resembles the pineapple in taste. The fruits fall when ripe and must stored in cool places until they are ready to be eaten. They are eaten as they are or are used to make jam, jelly, etc. It is used as a garden plant too.

Ficus aspera.

FICUS ASPERA

Ficus aspera G. Forst. [*F. parcellii* Veitch.].
Family: Moraceae.
Propagation: air layering.

Common name: CLOWN FIG.
Geographical distribution: Pacific Islands.

Evergreen small tree or large shrub. Oblong-oval leaves with asymmetric base, dentated, acuminate, hairy, especially beneath, up to 20 cm long, with irregular dark and light green and cream white spots. Tricolored fruit, green, white and red, 3 cm in diameter.

It prefers well-drained soils and is fussy about temperature. It grows slowly. Although it is a very beautiful species it is seldom seen in gardens. It is used as indoor plant.

FICUS AURICULATA

Ficus auriculata Lour. *[F. roxburghii* Wallich ex Miq.].
Family: *Moraceae.*
Geographical distribution: Himalaya.

Common name: HIMALAYAN FIG. TREE.
Propagation: by air layering and cuttings.

Ficus auriculata.

Deciduous shrub or tree up to 6 m high. Leaves broadly ovate or rounded. Petioles long, up to 25 cm long or more. Limbs acute or acuminate, cordate base, up to 45 cm long. Fruit pear-shaped or somewhat globose, yellowish or reddish, up to 6 cm in diameter or more, appearing on branches and trunk.
Tolerates most soils. Prefers a sunny site, although it withstands the shade. Slow growing.
Very ornamental, used in parks and gardens.

FICUS BENJAMINA

Ficus benjamina L.
Family: *Moraceae.*
Geographical distribution: India, Southeast Asia, Malay Archipielago and Australia.
Propagation: seeds, stem cutting and air layering.

Evergreen tree resembling a weeping willow, reaching heights of up to 20 m. Ovate-ellyptical, acuminate leaves, 10-12 cm long, glossy. Globose fruits, approximately 1 cm in diameter, red when ripe.
It accepts most soils. It is affected by the cold and the wind. It grows best when the soil is damp.Slow growing.
This tree is suitable for road sides and parks. It is widely used as an indoor plant in flowerpots.

Ficus benjamina.

FICUS ELASTICA

Ficus elastica Roxb. ex Hornem.   **Common name:** RUBBER TREE.
Family: *Moraceae.*   **Propagation:** stem cutting and air layering.
Geographical distribution: from Nepal to Assam and Burma.

Ficus elastica.

Evergreen tree up to 30 m tall. Oblong to ellyptical, leathery, shiny leaves, up to 30 cm long, enveloped in involucral, yellowish stipules with pink hues before blooming. Axillary fruits, usually in pairs, oblong ovate, yellow-greenish in color, up to 3 cm long.
Cv. Variegata, with pale green leaves and white or yellow edges.
Cv. Decora, with larger, wider leaves, dark green and with red stipules.
It prefers sunny, warm areas with abundant water. It is not too demanding concerning the soil and it grows fast.
It has been cultivated in Malaysia and India for extracting its rubber. It was also used as an indoor plant, although it is being substituted by its cultivars. In gardening it must only be used in parks and squares with enough space for its development. It must not be planted near buildings owing to its aggressive roots.

FICUS LYRATA

Ficus lyrata Warb. [*F. pandurata* Hort. Sander, non Hance.].
Family: *Moraceae.* **Geographical distribution:** Tropical western Africa.
Propagation: stem cutting and air layering.

Ficus lyrata.

Evergreen tree reaching a height of 12 m tall when cultivated, but up to 25 m tall when growing in its natural habitat. Large, violin-shaped leaves, coriaceous, shiny above and up to 40 cm long. Globose fruits, up to 5 cm in diameter, purple with white spots when ripe.
It tolerates most soils but prefers rich, well-drained areas, with a high humidity factor. It is affected by the cold.
This is a very decorative species thanks to its large, odd leaves. It is cultivated in gardens and parks and is also used as an indoor plant.

FICUS MACROPHYLLA

Ficus macrophylla Desf. ex Pers. [*F. macrocarpa* Hügel ex Kunth et Bouché].
Family: *Moraceae.* **Geographical distribution:** Australia.
Propagation: stem cutting.

Evergreen tree up to 40 m tall although in the Canary Islands it does not grow taller than 15 m. The trunk is gray and the oldest trees show aerial roots. Entire, ovate-elliptical leaves, dark green above, rusty colored beneath, up too 25 cm long, provided with long petioles. The terminal bud of the shoots is over 10 cm long and yellowish in color. Globose, axillary fruit up to 2.5 cm in diameter, purple with paler spots.
It accepts most soils and is fairly cold resistant. It stands the proximity of the sea.
Owing to its large size it must be cultivated in parks or large gardens. When young it can be used as an indoor plant in flowerpots.

Ficus macrophylla.

FICUS MICROCARPA

Ficus microcarpa L.f.   **Common name:** CHINESE BANYAN.
Family: *Moraceae.*   **Geographical distribution:** Tropical Asia and Malaysia.
Propagation: stem cutting and air layering.

Ficus microcarpa.

Evergreen tree up to 20 m tall. Ellyptical, glossy leaves, up to 16 cm long. Globose fruits, yellowish or reddish, blackish when mature, up to 1 cm in diameter.

It grows well on most soils, but prefers sunny, damp areas. It can grow near the sea and grows fast. It accepts thorough pruning.

It is used to line streets as well as in parks and gardens. Its powerful roots lift pavements and delve into pipes in their search for water, it must therefore be planted away from buildings, unless preventive measures are taken.

FICUS PUMILA

Ficus pumila L. *[F. stipulata* Thunb.; *F. repens* Hort., not Willd.].
Family: *Moraceae.*
Geographical distribution: Eastern Asia.
Propagation: usually, by cuttings and air layering.

Evergreen climber. Branches with fruit erect. with leaves elliptical or oblong, entire, with margins revolute, glossy green above and paler beneath, up to 10 cm long. Fruitless branches adventitious roots, which it uses to fix itself and climb, and leaves sessile or shortly petiolate, cordate-ovate, up to 6 cm long and 4 cm in diameter.

Takes to most soils. Can live in strong sun as well as in shade. Slow growing. Used in gardening to cover walls, pergolas, etc.

Ficus pumila.

FICUS RUBIGINOSA

Ficus rubiginosa Desf. ex Venten *[F. australis* Willd.].
Family: *Moraceae.*
Geographical distribution: Australia.
Common name: RUSTY FICUS.
Propagation: stem cutting and air layering.

Evergreen tree that in the Canary Islands reaches heights of 8 to 12 m, whereas its Australian biotype is either a shrub or a large tree. From its branches hang numerous red roots. Leathery, oval or ellyptical leaves up to 10 cm long, dark, glossy green above and rusty tomentous beneath. Small, globular fruits with reddish tones, about 1 cm in diameter.

It accepts different kinds of soils but prefers well-drained areas. It stands the vicinity of the sea and its root system is not as penetrating as with other species of Ficus. It is affected by the wind.

It is used as roadside and shade-giving tree. It is also planted indoors, in flowerpots.

Ficus rubiginosa

Ficus sycomorus.

FICUS SYCOMORUS

Ficus sycomorus L.
Family: *Moraceae.*
Common name: SYCAMORE FIG.
Geographical distribution: Egypt, Syria, Sudan through South Africa.
Propagation: seeds, stem cutting and air layering.

Evergreen tree, although in the Canary Islands it sheds some of its leaves; it grows to be over 20 m tall. The leaves have long petioles, and are oval or almost orbicular, up to 20 cm long, dark green above, lighter beneath, with hairy veins on this side. Unisexual, tiny flowers, grouped inside fleshy, pyriform receptacles, with only one opening on the apex, forming branched racemes on the trunk and branches, or else alone in the axils of the leaves. The fruit comes in small drupes clustered inside the receptable forming a pyriform infructescence in syconus, up to 3 cm long. The syconus are the figs, densely covered with whitish hair, green-yellowish with red hues in color.

It grows well on most soils but prefers sunny areas. In Africa it grows along the banks of rivers and watercourses, although it can be seen in the plains. It is affected by the cold.
The fruit is edible and is eaten by some African people. It is also eaten by birds, monkeys and other animals. This is the sycamore tree mentioned in the Bible. The wood was used by the Egyptians to make the sarcophagi for their mummies. Owing to its large size it is only grown in public parks and gardens.

GARDENIA CORNUTA

Gardenia cornuta Hemsl.
Family: *Rubiaceae.*
Flowering period: summer.

Geographical distribution: South Africa.
Propagation: by seed and cutting.

Gardenia cornuta. Detail.

Evergreen shrub or small tree, up to 4.5 m high, with branches erect and twigs sometimes spiny. Leaves opposite or verticillate, obovate to oblanceolate, up to 12.5 cm long. Flowers hermaphrodite, solitary, fragrant, appearing at the end of sprigs. Calyx tubular, with six cylindrical appendages that stick out laterally close to the end. Corolla salverform, up to 6.5 cm in diameter, with tube greenish-white up to 7.5 cm long and white lobes. Fruits in berries, oval or pyriform, golden and up to 5 cm long.

Prefers soils rich in organic matter and an adequate water supplement. Needs a sunny or partially sunny location. Somewhat resistant to cold and drought. Slow growing. The Zulus prepare an infusion with the fruit and roots which they use as an emetic. The wood is used for fences and firewood. In gardening it is used individually or in groups.

Gardenia cornuta.

66

GARDENIA THUNBERGIA

Gardenia thunbergia L.
Family: *Rubiaceae.*
Flowering period: summer.

Geographical distribution: South Africa.
Propagation: by seed and cuttings.

Gardenia thunbergia.

Evergreen shrub up to 3 m high. Leaves opposite or verticillate, elliptical, up to 18 cm long. Flowers hermaphrodite, solitary, fragrant, appearing at the end of the sprigs. Calyx tubular, with a terminal cleft, with foliaceous appendages. Corolla salverform, up to 7.5 cm in diameter, with tube greenish-white, up to 6 cm long and limb formed by eight white overlapping lobes. Fruits in berries, ovoid, woody, grayish, up to 5 cm long or more.

Prefers good quality soils and regular watering. Suitable for bright sun or partial shade. Somewhat resistant to cold and drought. Slow growing.

The roots are used for treating skin eruptions and as an emetic. The wood for making tools, etc.

In gardening used individually or in groups.

Gardenia thunbergia.

GINKGO BILOBA

Ginkgo biloba L.
Family: *Ginkgoaceae.*
Geographical distribution: China.

Common name: GINKGO, MAIDEN-HAIR TREE.
Flowering period: spring.
Propagation: seeds, stem cutting, air layering and grafting.

Ginkgo biloba.

Deciduous, dioecious tree, up to 35 m tall. Macroblasts with scattered leaves. Brachyblasts with a rosette of flowers in the apexes. Fan-shaped leaves up to 14 cm long, with long petioles, entire or with a cleft in the central part starting at the apex. The male flowers are clustered in amentiform, lax strobiles. The female flowers are in groups of two on long peduncles. Yellowish seeds, resembling drupes, up to 2.5 cm long.
This tree prefers rich, well-drained soils in sunny areas and is resistant to cold. It grows slowly.
The Ginkgo is considered as a «Living fossil» since it is the only survivor of an extinct race. The edible seeds are considered delicacies in China and Japan.
It is used to line avenues and streets and to give shade tree in parks and gardens. Only male trees are used, for when the seeds of the female trees fall to the ground, they release an unpleasant butyric acid smell.

GOETHEA STRICTIFLORA

Goethea strictiflora Hook.
Family: *Malvaceae.*
Flowering period: nearly year-round.

Geographical distribution: Brazil.
Propagation: usually by cuttings.

Goethea Strictiflora.

Evergreen shrub up to 2 m high. Leaves alternate, ovate to ovate-elliptical, coriaceous, sinuate-dentate, up to 30 cm long or more. Flowers hermaphrodite clustered in cymes, appearing on very short sprigs along the stem. Flowers are protected by four bracts (calyculus) ocordate to triangular or ovate, reddish, up to 2 cm long. Calyx pentalobed. Corolla more or less tubular. Fruit in schizocarp.
Not particular regarding soil. Prefers sunny location, although it accepts some shade.
In gardening used individually or to form groups.

Grevillea banksii.

GREVILLEA BANKSII

Grevillea banksii R. Br.
Family: *Proteaceae.*
Flowering period: almost entire year.

Geographical distribution: Australia.
Propagation: seeds and stem cutting.

Evergreen shrub or small tree reaching a height of up to 6 m. Pinnately parted leaves up to 25 cm long. Linear or lanceolate segments, up to 10 cm long, silky-tomentous beneath. Red or sometimes white flowers, clustered in racemes up to 18 cm long.

It prefers well drained soils and sunny areas, for in the shade its flowering decreases. It avoids limestone and is killed off by frosts. It grows fast. This shrub is often seen in groups or standing alone. The inflorescences can be used as bouquet flowers.

Grevillea robusta.

GREVILLEA ROBUSTA

Grevillea robusta A. Cunn.
Family: *Proteaceae.*
Flowering period: spring-summer.

Common name: GREVILLEA, SILKY OAK.
Geographical distribution: Australia.
Propagation: seeds and stem cutting.

Evergreen tree raching heights of up to 30 m. although it is usually smaller when cultivated. Pinnate or nearly bipinnate leaves up to 35 cm long, with whitish folioles beneath, resembling the fronds of a fern. Golden yellow flowers clustered in racemes up to 15 cm long. Fruit in folicule, dark brown to blackish in color, up to 18 mm long and with 1 or 2 seeds.
It tolerates most kinds of soils although it requires sunny areas to flower properly. It stands cold weather and drought and grows fast.
Its good quality wood is used for barrel and cabinet-making. This is a very spectacular tree when it flowers. It is used to line streets as well as in parks and gardens. When young it is used as indoor plant.

HAEMANTHUS PUNICEUS (SCADOXUS PUNICEUS)

Scadoxus puniceus (L.) Friis et Nordal *[Haemanthus puniceus L.]*
Family: *Amaryllidaceae.*
Flowering period: winter.

Geographical distribution: South Africa.
Propagation: by seed and division.

Haemanthus puniceus (Scadoxus puniceus).

Plant bulbous with leaves oblong, slender, undulated, acute, spotted with purple in the basal part, up to 55 cm long and 14 cm wide. Flowers hermaphrodite clustered in umbellate capitula up to 12 cm in diameter appearing at the end of a scape pale green in colour with purple dots at the base, thick, fleshy, up to 55 cm long or more. Bracts tinted purple. Perianth corolline, light scarlet to white, up to 3 cm long, with tube shorter than the narrow, erect segments. Stamens exserted, with yellow anthers. Fruits in berries.

Prefers rich, well drained soils. Grows better in a shady site, although it accepts bright sun.

Used in gardening to form groups. Also as potted plant.

HEDYCHIUM CORONARIUM

Hedychium coronarium J. König.
Family: *Zingiberaceae.*
Flowering period: late summer-autumn.

Geographical distribution: Tropical Asia.
Propagation: by seed and division.

Hedychium coronarium.

Perennial, herbaceous, rhizomatous plant, up to 1.80 m high, with many stems. Leaves alternate, distichous, oblong-lanceolate to lanceolate, sheathing, hairy underneath, up to 60 cm long. Flowers hermaphrodite, white, fragant, clustered in spikes. Tube of corolla slender, up to 8.5 cm long. Lobes of corolla narrow. Staminode lip large, approx. 5 cm long, bilobed, sometimes with yellow spot on base. Staminodes lateral similar to petals. Fruits in capsules. Needs rich soil and abundant moisture. Prefers partially shady site. Fast growing.
Used in gardening to form groups. Also as potted plant.

HEDYCHIUM GARDNERIANUM

Hedychium gardnerianum Roscoe.
Family: *Zingiberaceae.*
Flowering period: summer-autumn.

Geographical distribution: India.
Propagation: by seed and division.

Perennial, herbaceous, rhizomatous plant, up to 1.80 m high or more. Leaves alternate, distichous, sheating, glabrous, lanceolate or oblong-lanceolate glaucous beneath, up to 40 cm long. Flowers hermaphrodite, yellow, fragant, clustered in spikes up to 30 cm long or more. Tube of corolla up to 5.5 cm long, with lobes linear, involute and recurved. Staminode lip bilobed, up to 3 cm long. Filament of stamen red, exserted. Fruits in capsules.
Requires rich soil and abundant moisture. Prefers partially sunny site. Fast growing. Hardier than the rest of the hedychium species grown.
Used in gardening to form groups. Also as potted plant.

HELICONIA BIHAI

Heliconia bihai (L.) L. *[H. humilis* Jacq.; *H. caribaea* auct. non Lam.].
Family: *Musaceae.*
Propagation: by seed and division.
Geographical distribution: West Indies and Nothern south America.

Common name: BALISIER.
Flowering period: summer-autumn

Herbaceous, rhizomatous plant, with musroid growing habit, up to 5 m high. Leaves distichous, oblong, acuminate. Petioles usually glabrous, up to 110 cm long. Limbs up to 100 cm long or more. Inflorescence erect up to 65 cm long. Spathes distichous to irregularly arranged, not reflexed at the end, up to 30 cm long, glabrous to somewhat hairy, boat-shaped, red on sides, yellow in the carina and margins yellow and/or green. Spathes not overlapping or only at the base, containing several greenish flowers clustered in cincinnus. Fruits in capsules.
Prefers rich soils and abundant moisture. Better in a sunny or partially sunny site. Fast growing.
In gardening used to form groups. Also grown for cut flowers.

Heliconia bihai.

Hedychium gardnerianum. ▶

HIBISCUS ROSA-SINENSIS

Hibiscus rosa-sinensis L.
Family: *Malvaceae.*
Flowering period: throughout the year.

Common name: CHINESE HIBISCUS, ROSE OF CHINA.
Geographical distribution: Asia.
Propagation: stem cutting.

Evergreen shrub that can reach a height of 4 m. Oval leaves, dentate on their apical part, up to 15 cm long. Large, red flowers that grow alone at the axils of the leaves. Fruits in capsule.
It prefers rich soils, although it can grow in less favorable conditions. Needs the sun to flower properly. Fast growing.
The flowers of this tree are used in some countries as a hair dye and for shining shoes. In Hawaii the flowers are used to make necklaces to welcome tourists.

Hibiscus rosa-sinensis.

HIBISCUS SCHIZOPETALUS

Hibiscus schizopetalus (M. T. Mast) Hook.f.
Common name: JAPANESE HIBISCUS.
Flowering period: autumn-winter.

Family: *Malvaceae.*
G. distribution: Tropical Eastern Africa.
Propagation: stem cutting.

Evergreen shrub up to 3 m tall with thin branches. Simple ellyptical-ovate, dentate leaves, up to 16 cm long. Pendular flowers on long peduncles. Petals up to 6 cm long, curved, laciniated and red-pink in color. Fruit in capsules.
It requires rich soils, well-drained and highly humid. It prefers rather shady areas and its growth pace is fast.
It is widely used in gardens in tropical and subtropical countries. It can be cultivated alone or forming groups. It has also been seen used as a climbing tree to cover an arbour.

Hibiscus schizopetalus.

HOWEA BELMOREANA

Howea belmoreana (C. Moore et F. J. Muell) Becc.
[Kentia belmoreana C. Moore et F. J. Muell.]
Family: *Palmae.*
Geographical distribution: Lord Howe's Island.
Common name: BELMOR SENTRY PALM.
Propagation: seeds.

Monoecious palm up to 7.9 m tall with ringed trunk. Pinnate leaves, up to 2 m long, very arched and with quite short petioles. Erect pinnae approximately 2.5 cm wide. Flowers in triads (2 male and 1 female), arranged along spikes that sprout alone in the axils of leaves and provided with long peduncles. Ellipsoidal fruits, up to 3.5 cm long, green-yellowish in color. This palm prefers loam, rich, well-drained soils. It grows well both in the sun or in shady areas and its growth pace is slow.
It is used for indoor decoration as well as in park and gardens, either alone or in groups. It is also seen growing along streets and avenues.

Howea belmoreana.

77

Howea belmoreana.

HOWEA FORSTERIANA

Howea forsteriana (C. Moore et F. J. Muell.) Becc.
[Kentia forsteriana C. Moore et F. J. Muell.].
Family: *Palmae.*
Common name: KENTIA.

Geographical distribution: Lord Howe's Island.
Propagation: seeds.

Howea forsteriana.

Monoecious palm reaching a height of over 18 m. Pinnate leaves, up to 3 m long, straight when young and bending with age. Long petioles. Horizontal pinnae or somewhat pendular. The flowers appear in triads along spikes provided with long peduncles. Spikes in groups of 3.6 formed in the axils of the leaves. Ellipsoidal fruits up to 3.5 cm long, green-yellowish in color. Not fussy about soil, although it prefers loam, rich, well-drained soil. It grows either in the sun or in the shade and it grows fast. This is one of the most palm populars, widely used for indoor decoration. It is also cultivated in gardens both alone and in groups. It is also used to line

79

HYMENOCALLIS LITTORALIS

Hymenocallis littoralis (Jacq.) Salisb.
Family: *Amaryllidaceae.*
Flowering period: summer-autumn.

Geographical distribution: Tropical America.
Propagation: by seed and division.

Hymenocallis littoralis.

Acaulescent, bulbous, herbaceous plant, losing its leaves in winter. These are basal, strap-shaped, canaliculate, up to 1 m long and approx. 4 cm wide. Flowers hermaphrodite, white, fragrant, arranged in umbel at the end of a floral scape longer than the leaves. Perianth salverform. Tube up to 16 cm long or more. Lobes linear, up to 11 cm long or more, curved. Crown funnel-shaped joining base of the six stamen. Free part of filaments up to 7 cm long. Style longer than stamens.
Not particular regarding soil. Prefers partially shady site. Grows poorly near the sea.
In gardening used to form groups. Also as potted plant.

IOCHROMA CYANEUM

Iochroma cyaneum (Lindl.) M. L. Green.
[I. lanceolatum (Miers) Miers; *I. tubulosum* Benth.].
Family: *Solanaceae.*
F. period: almost throughout the year.

G. distribution: North-western South America.
Propagación: by seed ant stem cutting.

Evergreen shrub up to 3 m tall. Entire, alternate, ovate-lanceolate leaves, up to 20 cm long, acute to acuminate. Tubular flowers provided with long peduncles. The corolla can reach up to 5 cm long, with tones ranging from dark blue to blue-purple. Fruit in berries.

Iochroma cyaneum.

IPOMOEA ACUMINATA

Ipomoea acuminata (Vahl) Roem. et Schult.
[*I. learii* Paxt.]
Family: *Convolvulaceae.*
Geographical distribution: Tropical America.
Flowering period: nearly all year.
Propagation: by seed and cuttings.

It does not require special soils. It prefers sunny areas although it can live in shaded areas.
It in used in tropical and subtropical gardens and is seen alone and in groups.

Climber evergreen. Leaves broadly ovate to orbicular, cordate, entire or three-lobed, pubescent underneath, up to 15 cm long. Flowers hermaphrodite clustered in racemes. Calyx pubescent, with sepals acuminate. Corolla funnel-shaped, pink-purple in colour, up to 8 cm long and same in diameter, with 10 strias. Fruits in capsules. Not particular about soil. Requires sunny location. Fast growing.
Used in gardening to cover walls, fences, pergolas, etc.

Ipomoea acuminata.

IPOMOEA HORSFALLIAE

Ipomoea horsfalliae Hook.
Family: *Convolvulaceae.*
Flowering period: nearly all year.

Geographical distribution: West Indies.
Propagation: by seed and cuttings.

Climber woody, evergreen. Leaves palmate-lobed to palmatisect, with 5-7 lobes, thick, glabrous, up to 16.5 cm long. Flowers hermaphrodite, clustered in dichotomous cymes. Corolla campanulate, pink o purple, up to 4 cm long and 4 cm in diameter. Fruits in capsules.
Accepts most soils. Prefers sunny location. Tolerates being near the sea.
In gardening used to cover pergolas, walls, etc.

Ipomoea horsfalliae.

IRESINE HERBSTII

Iresine herbstii Hook. *[I. reticulata* Hort.; *Achyranthes herbstii* Hort.].
Family: *Amaranthaceae.*
Geographical distribution: South America.

Common name: BEEF PLANT.
Propagation: by cuttings.

Perennial herb, up to 1.80 m high, with stem and branches reddish. Leaves opposite, broadly ovate to orbicular, obtuse, emarginated, red-purple, with nervations lighter coloured. Limbs up to 9.5 cm long. Petioles up to 8 cm long. Flowers small, whitish, clustered in spikes arranged in panicles. Fruit in utricle, indehiscent.
Prefers rich, well drained soils and abundant water. Needs sunny site.
Accepts trimming. Fast growing.
Used in gardening to form masses of colour and for hedges.

Iresine herbstii.

IRESINE HERBSTII CV AUREO-RETICULATA

Iresine herbstii Hook. Cv. Aureo-reticulata.
Family: *Amaranthaceae.*   **Common name:** AQUIRANTE.
Propagation: by cuttings.

Herb perennial, up to 1.80 m high, with stem and branches reddish. Leaves opposite, broadly ovate, acute to acuminate, green with yellowish nervations. Limbs up to 17 cm long. Petioles reddish, up to 6 cm long. Flowers small, whitish, clustered in spikes arranged in panicles. Fruit in utricle, indehiscent.
Prefers rich, well drained soils and abundant moisture. Requires sunny situation. Fast growing. Accepts trimming.
Used in gardening to form masses of colour and for hedges.

Iresine herbstii Cv. Aureo-reticulata.

JACARANDA MIMOSIFOLIA

Jacaranda mimosifolia D. Don. *[J. ovalifolia* R. Br.].
Common name: JACARANDA.
G. distribution: Brazil, Argentina and Uruguay.

Family: *Bignoniaceae.*
Flowering period: spring-summer.
Propagation: seeds and stem cutting.

Jacaranda mimosifolia.

Deciduous tree reaching heights of up to 15 m. Compound, bipinnate leaves up to 80 cm long. Oblong-rhomboidal leaflets. Blue flowers up to 5 cm long, clustered in pendular terminal panicles. Fruit in capsules, flat, suborbicular and up to 7 cm long, holding numerous alate seeds.
It grows on most soils and stands cold weather rather well. It is seen in Mediterranean countries. Fast growing. It requires sunny areas and its wood is appreciated for cabinet-making.
This is a very beautiful tree, especially when it flowers. It is generally used to line streets as well as in parks and gardens.

JASMINUM AZORICUM

Jasminum azoricum L.
Family: *Oleaceae.*
Flowering period: nearly year-round.

Geographical distribution: Madeira.
Propagation: usually by cuttings.

Jasminum azoricum.

Climbing shrub evergreen. Leaves opposite, trifoliolate, with folioles ovate, acute to acuminate, undulated, glossy green above and lighter beneath. Side folioles shortly petiolate, smaller than the terminal, reaching 10 cm in length. Flowers hermaphrodite, fragrant, clustered in axillary and terminal cymes. Corolla salverform up to 2.5 cm in diameter, white with purple tints in the tube and outer part of lobes, which are more or less lanceolate. Fruits in berries.
Accepts most soils. Prefers sunny location. Somewhat slow growing. Used in gardening to cover walls, pergolas, etc.

JASMINUM MESNYI

Jasminum mesnyi Hance *[J. primulinum* Hemsl.]
Family: *Oleaceae.*
Geographical distribution: China.
Propagation: normally by cuttings.

Common name: JAPANESE JASMINE.
Flowering period: winter-spring.

Evergreen shrub up to 3 m high, with branches quadrangular. Leaves opposite, trifoliolate, with spiny margins, dark green above and lighter beneath. Side folioles sessile, smaller than terminal, reaching 11 cm in length. Flowers hermaphrodite, solitary, in axils of leaves, often

Jasminum mesnyi.

double, 3-4.5 cm in diameter. Corolla yellow, salverform, with orange strias in narrow part. Short tube. Not particular regarding soil. Prefers sunny location. Somewhat resistant to frost.
Used in gardening to cover walls.

Jasminum mesnyi. Detalle.

JASMINUM POLYANTHUM

Jasminum polyanthum Franch.
Family: *Oleaceae.*
Flowering period: winter-spring.

Geographical distribution: China.
Propagation: by seed and cuttings.

*Jasminum
polyanthum.*

Deciduous shrub, sometimes evergreen, usually climber. Leaves opposite, pinnate, with 5-7 folioles lanceolate, trinerviate from base, lighter beneath. Bases of petioles broad, almost winged, more or less amplexicaul. Side folioles shorter than terminal, reaching 8 cm in length. Flowers hermaphrodite, fragrant, up to 3 cm in diameter, clustered in axillary panicles. Calyx five-lobed, with lobes subulate, not exceeding 2 mm long. Corolla white, salverform, with rosaceous tints on tube and outer part of lobes. Tube 20-22 mm long. Lobes 4-5. Fruits in berries.
Prefers rich, well drained soils and a sunny location. Fast growing. Shows some resistance to frost.
Used in gardening to cover pergolas, walls, etc.

JUBAEA CHILENSIS

Jubaea chilensis (Mol.) Baill. [*J. spectabilis* HBK.].
Family: *Palmae.*
Propagation: seeds.

Common name: Chilean wine palm tree.

Monoecious palm reaching a height of up to 25 m. Very thick trunk, up to 1.8 m in diameter. Pinnate leaves, green or greyish green, up to 4 m long. Short petioles with smooth edges. Inflorescences measuring over 90 cm in length, brown and appearing among the leaves. Ovoidal, yellow fruits, up to 3.5 cm long.

Jubaea Chilensis.

It accepts most soils but requires sunny areas. It withstands cold weather, even when it gets as cold as -7º C.

The sap, concentrated by boiling, produces the exquisite palm honey, and is fermented to make palm wine. This production involves the felling of the tree and has led to the disappearance of many natural woods of this species. For some years now it has been protected by law. The fruit is edible.

This palm tree is cultivated in parks and gardens in Mediterranean countries.

JUSTICIA AUREA

Justicia aurea Schlechtend. *[J. umbrosa* Benth.; *Jacobinia aurea* (Schlechtend.) Hemsl., not Hiern].
Family: *Acanthaceae.*
F. period: end of autumn-winter.
G. distribution: Mexico and Central America.
Propagation: normally by cuttings.

Justicia aurea.

Shrub evergreen up to 3.5 m high, with stems and branches obtusely quadrangular. Leaves opposite, ovate or lanceolate-oblong, with prominent veins beneath, up to 40 cm long, decurrent, acuminate. Petioles up to 8 cm long. Flowers hermaphrodite, in dense terminal spikes, up to 18 cm long. Bracts and sepals linear-lanceolate, tinted purple. Corolla yellow, tubular, bilabiate, curved, open almost half-way, up to 8 cm long. Fruits in capsules. Prefers rich, well drained soils. Requires abundant water. Although it accepts bright sun, it grows better in partially shady spots. Fast growing. Should be pruned after flowering.
Used in gardening to form groups or individually.

JUSTICIA RIZZINII

Justicia rizzinii Wassh. *[J. floribunda* Hort.; *J. pauciflora* (Nees) Griseb., non Vahl; *Jacobinia pauciflora* (Nees) Lindau].
Family: *Acanthaceae.*
Flowering period: late of autumn-winter-spring.
Geographical distribution: Brazil.
Propagación: by seed and cuttings.

Shrub evergreen up to 60 cm high. Branches pubescent. Leaves opposite, entire, elliptical o elliptical-oblong, acute to acuminate, up to 3.5 m long. Each pair of leaves are slightly unequal in size. Petioles short. Flowers

Justicia rizzinii.

hermaphrodite, clustered in axillary spikes with few flowers,
semipendulous or pendulous. Corolla tubular, angular, bilabiate, with basal
part red and apical part yellow, up to 2.5 cm long. Fruits in capsules.
Prefers rich, well drained soils. Although it accepts bright sun, it grows
better in partially shady sites. Slow growing.
Used in gardening as solitary plant or to form groups. Also as potted plant.

Justicia rizzinii.

KIGELIA AFRICANA

Kigelia africana (Lam.) Benth.
Family: Bignoniaceae.
Flowering period: summer-autumn.

Common name: SAUSAGE TREE.
Geographical distribution: Tropical Africa.
Propagation: seeds.

Kigelia africana.

Semideciduous tree reaching heights of up to 15 m. Imparipinnate leaves 30 cm or more in length. There are usually 7 to 11 elliptical-oblong or obovate folioles, up to 14 cm long. Bell-shaped flowers, blood red in color, up to 10 cm long, clustered in pendular panicles. Elongated, sausage-like fruits, up to 60 cm long, hanging from long peduncles.

This tree accepts most soils and is partially drought resistant. Should not be grown in cold areas. Fast growing. When the fruit is crushed or ground it is used for healing skin ulcers, syphilis and rheumatism. The fruit is also baked and added as a flavoring substance in the beermaking process. The wood is utilized to make canoes.

This tree is seen in large gardens and parks and is also used to line streets.

LAGUNARIA PATERSONII

Lagunaria patersonii (Andr.) G. Don.
Family: *Malvaceae.*

Common name: NORFOLK ISLAND HIBISCUS.
Geographical distribution: Australia, Norfolk Island and Lord Howe's Island.
Flowering period: spring-summer.

Propagation: seeds.

Evergreen tree up to 13 m tall. Entire, oblong or oval-oblong leaves, greyish-green, up to 14 cm long. Bell-shaped flowers, up to 6.5 cm long, resembling hibiscus flowers, pink in color, growing alone or in clusters. Obovoid to ellipsoidal fruit in capsules, up to 4.5 cm long, with a large amount of hairs that irritate the skin.

It requires well-drained soils. Very resistant to sea mist; for this reason it is an adequate species to grow on coastal plantations. It prefers open, sunny areas and is has some resistance to cold weather. It is used to line city streets and in gardens in general.

Lagunaria patersonii.

LANTANA CAMARA

Lantana camara L.
Family: *Verbenaceae.*
F. period: almost thoughout the year.

Common name: YELLOW SAGE.
Geographical distribution: Tropical America.
Propagation: seeds and stem cutting.

Lantana camara.

Evergreen shrub 1 1/2 - 2 m tall, hairy and sometimes thorny. Opposite, ovate to oblong-ovate leaves, dentated-crenulated, up to 11 cm long. Flowers small, yellow-orange or orange, then turning red, clustered in axilar and terminal capitula, up to 3.5 cm in diameter. Fruits in drupes, blackish, approximately 3 mm in diameter.
Not fussy about soil, although it prefers well-drained, rich ground. It requires the sun and grows fast. It has to be pruned back when it becomes too leggy or woody.
This shrub is used for home medicinal purposes. It is widely used in gardening and can be planted either alone or forming hedges.

LEUCOSPERMUM CORDIFOLIUM

Leucospermum cordifolium (Salisb. ex Knight) Fourcade *[L. nutans* R. Br.].
Family: *Proteaceae.*
Geographical distribution: South Africa.
Propagation: by seed and cuttings.

Common name: NODDING PINCUSHION.
Flowering period: late winter-spring.

Evergreen shrub up to 1.5 m high and about 2 m in diameter, with branches extending horizontally. Leaves ovate, ocordate and entire to oblong-obtuse and with up to six teeth in the apex, up to 8 cm long, pubescent first and later glabrous. Flowers hermaphrodite, clustered in capitula up to 12 cm in diameter. Perianth up to 3.5 cm long. Style

adaxially curved near its apex, up to 6 cm long. The perianth and style are usually orange although sometimes there are plants with yellow or red ones. Fruits are achenes, whitish. Needs acid soil, preferably sandy-loam, with low salt content, but well drained. Requires sunny site. Sensitive to frost. Slow growing.

Grown for its extremely beautiful flowers, very long lasting in water after cut, about two weeks, although with a floral preserver they can last four weeks or more.

In gardening used individually or in groups.

Leucospernum cordifolium.

LIVISTONA CHINENSIS

Livistona chinensis (Jacq.) R. Br. ex Mart. var. *chinensis*.
Family: *Palmae.*   **Common name:** CHINESE FAN PALM.
Geographical distribution: Japan, China.   **Propagation:** seeds.

Livistona chinensis.

Monoecioius palm reaching a height of 9 m or more. Palmate leaves, up to 3 m long. Petioles with dentated bases. Limbs divided into many segments with pendular apexes. Branched inflorescences that sprout among the leaves. Hermaphrodite flowers in cincinnus of up to 6 flowers, white in color. Ellipsoidal fruits, bluish-green to green, up to 2 cm long.

It prefers rich soils, well-drained, and very humid. It thrives both in the sun and in shaded areas. It grows slowly.

In China the leaves are used to make fans.

This is a very ornamental palm tree widely used in tropical and subtropical countries. It is seen in parks and gardens and is also used for interior decoration and in courtyards as flowerpot plant.

LYTOCARIUM WEDDELLIANUM

Lytocarium weddellianum (H. Wendl.)
Toledo [*Microcoelum weddellianum* (H. Wendl) H. E. Moore.].
Family: *Palmae.*   **Common name:** WEDDEL'S PALM.
Geographical distribution: Brazil.   **Propagation:** seeds.

Monoecious palm with a long, slender trunk, up to 5 cm in diameter and 3 m tall. Pinnate leaves up to 1.20 m long. Narrowly linear pinnae up to 25 cm long and up to 8 mm wide, glaucous beneath. Spineless petioles. The inflorescences appear among the flowers in simple ramification patterns, up to 90 cm long, provided with small unisexual flowers. Ovoid fruits up to 2.5 cm long.

It prefers rich, well-drained soils, partly shady. It grows slowly.

This species is extensively cultivated as flowerpot plant. In gardening it is used alone or in groups.

Lytocarium weddellianum.

MACADAMIA INTEGRIFOLIA

Macadamia integrifolia Maiden et Betche.
Geographical distribution: Australia.
Flowering period: several times throughout the year.

Family: *Proteaceae.*
Common name: MACADAMIA NUT.
Propagation: seeds and grafting.

Macadamia integrifolia.

Evergreen tree that in Australia can reach a height of 18 m, but elsewhere rarely surpasses 9 m. When young the leaves are serrated-dentated and when adult they become oblong-lanceolated to obovate, 10-30 cm long. They are grouped in verticils usually made up of three leaves, although occasionally there are four. Whitish, fragrant, hermaphrodite flowers, in racemes up to 30 cm long. Globose fruits up to 3 cm in diameter, with one spherical or two semispherical seeds.

It grows upright, in dry or humid areas. It prefers well-drained soils and it grows slowly.

It is cultivated in tropical and subtropical regions. The seeds are very tasty, and are eaten raw or roasted. The wood is used for cabinet-making.

It is recommended as a shade-giving tree.

MACKAYA BELLA

Mackaya bella Harv. [*Asystasia bella* Hort.].
Family: *Acanthaceae.*
Flowering period: autumn-winter-spring.

Common name: MACKAYA.
Geographical distribution: South Africa.
Propagation: seeds and stem cutting.

Mackaya bella.

Evergreen shrub reaching a height of up to 2 m. Opposite, ovate-oblong, sinuated-dentated, acuminate leaves up to 14 cm long. Funnel-shaped, pale lavender flowers, with darker veins, up to 6 cm long, grouped in terminal racemes. Fruit in capsules, elongated, up to 7 cm long.
It needs rich, well-drained soils and prefers shady areas.
It is affected by cold weather and can be grown in coastal gardens.
It is widely used in gardening. It can be planted alone or in groups.

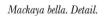

Mackaya bella. Detail.

MALVAVISCUS ARBOREUS

Malvaviscus arboreus Cav. [*M. mollis* (Ait.) DC.].
Family: *Malvaceae.*
Flowering period: nearly year-round.
G. distribution: Mexico to Peru and Brazil.
Propagation: by seed and cuttings.

Shrub evergreen, up to 3.5 m high. Leaves simple, alternate, lobulate or not, ovate to suborbicular, dentate, acuminate, densely pubescent, up to 20 cm or more. Flowers hermaphrodite, erect, usually solitary in axils of leaves. Corolla funnel-shaped, bright red, with petals convolute, about 3 cm long. Stamens joined in one tubular column longer than petals, in schizocarp.
Not particular about soil. Prefers sunny situation, although lives well in partial shade. Fast growing.
In gardening used individually, in groups and for hedges.

Malvaviscus arboreus. ▶

MAMMEA AMERICANA

Mammea americana L.
Family: *Guttiferae.*
F. period: autumn-winter.
Common name: MAMEY.
G. distribution: West Indies and northern South America.
Propagation: seeds and stem cutting.

Evergreen tree reaching heights of 20 m. Entire, oblong-obovate, leathery, leaves, shiny above, 20 to 22 cm long, and 10 cm wide. Polygamous flowers, white fragrant, solitary or in clusters in the branches. Globose fruits up to 15 cm in diameter, rusty in color, with 1-4 large seeds.
It prefers rich, well-drained, soils. It is affected by cold weather and can stand the proximity of the sea.
This is a very beautiful tree that resembles the magnolia tree. It is cultivated for the fruits that are similar in flavor to peaches. The fruits are eaten directly from the tree or are used to makes sauces, jams, preserves, etc. In Mexico the juice and seeds are used as insecticides. With the flowers is made a liqueur called «Créme de Créole.» The wood is of good quality.

Mammea americana.

MANDEVILLA LAXA

Mandevilla laxa (Ruiz et Pav.) Woodson *[M. suaveolens* Lindl.].
Family: *Apocynaceae.*   **Common name:** JASMINE OF CHILE.
G. distribution: Bolivia and northern Argentina.   **Flowering period:** Primavera-verano.
Propagation: by seed and cuttings.

Mandevilla laxa.

Climber woody, evergreen. Leaves opposite, ovate, with cordate base, acuminate, up to 22 cm long, hairy above and glabrous beneath, except for group of hairs in the axils of side veins. Petioles up to 5.5 cm long, with reddish tint. Flowers hermaphrodite, fragrant, grouped in racemes. Calyx 5-partite. Corolla funnel-shaped, white to creamy white, 5-lobed, up to 5 cm long and 8 cm in diameter. Fruits in follicles, cylindrical, up to 50 cm long. Not particular about soil. Prefers sunny location. Moderate growth. Used in gardening to cover pergolas, walls, etc.

MANGIFERA INDICA

Mangifera indica L.
Family: *Anacardiaceae.*   **Common name:** MANGO.
Geographical distribution: India.   **Propagation:** seeds, stem cutting and air layering.

Evergreen tree reaching a height of up to 30 m but usually smaller. Oblong-lanceolate to elliptical leaves, up to 25-30 cm long, dark green in color. Yellowish or pinkish flowers clustered in panicles. Edible fruits of different size, greenish, yellow or reddish.
It grows well on most soils, although it prefers rich, deep, well-drained ground. It dies in cold, damp weather. It requires warmer weather than the avocado tree and stands up to the wind better.

Mangifera indica.

When growing the tree shows a reddish hue which constitutes one of the most attractive characteristics of this tree. De Candolle affirms that this tree has been cultivated by man for over 4000 years. In Indian literature this tree is mentioned and praised.

Selected cultivars such as 'Haden', 'Irwin', 'Keitt', 'Zill', etc., produce a very tasty fruit which is usually eaten straight from the tree, although it is also used to make jams, etc. The unselected cultivars yield a fruit which is fibrous and turpentine like in flavor.

The leaves of the mango are used in Mexico for the cleaning of teeth and to harden gums.

In gardening it is used in gardens and parks as well as on roadsides.

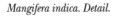

Mangifera indica. Detail.

MEGASKEPASMA ERYTHROCHLAMYS

Megaskepasma erythrochlamys Lindau.
Family: *Acanthaceae.*
Flowering period: autumn-winter.

Common name: BRAZILIAN REDCLOAK.
Geographical distribution: Venezuela.
Propagation: stem cutting.

Megaskepasma erythrochlamys.

Evergreen shrub up to 2 m tall. Elliptical to oblong-elliptical leaves with entire or ondulated edges, acuminate apex and cuneate base, up to 30 cm long. White or light pink flowers, grouped in terminal spikes up to 20 cm long. Red-purple, ovate to ovate-lanceolate bracts up to 4 cm long. Fruit in capsules.
It prefers well-drained soils, rich in organic matter. It can be cultivated in the sun, but it flowers best in semishady areas. It is affected by drought.
It is mainly cultivated in tropical and subtropical regions. It grows alone or in groups.

MERREMIA TUBEROSA

Merremia tuberosa (L.) Rendle *[Ipomoea tuberosa L.]*.
Family: *Convolvulaceae.*   **Common name:** WOOD ROSE.
Geographical distribution: probably from Tropical America.
Flowering period: autumn and spring.   **Propagation:** by seed and cuttings.

Merremia tuberosa. General aspect and detail.

Evergreen climber. Leaves palmatipartite, with seven segments oblong-lanceolate. Petioles long, up to 14 cm in length. Flowers hermaphrodite, tubular-funnel shaped, up to 5.5 cm in diameter. Corolla yellow. Flowers in clusters with varied number of flowers. Fruits in capsules, globose, irregularly  dehiscent, which when dry, look like a rose carved in wood. Accepts most soils. Requires sunny location. Drought-resistant. Fast growing.
Used in gardening to cover walls, fences and pergolas.

MONSTERA DELICIOSA

Monstera deliciosa Liebm. *[Philodendron pertusum* Kunth et Bouché].
Family: *Araceae.*
Common name: CERIMAN.
Geographical distribution: Mexico and Central America.
Propagation: normally by cuttings.

Two aspects of Monstera deliciosa.

Climber woody, evergreen, with aerial roots growing along the stem. Leaves large with limb cordate-ovate, pinnatifid, perforated with holes elliptical to oblong, coriaceous, up to 70 cm long. Petioles articulate, winged, as long as limbs. Flowers very small, arranged on a cylindrical spadix up to 25 cm long surrounded by a creamy spathe, curved. Flowers hermaphrodite, fertile, in upper part and sterile ones in lower part. Fruits in berries, small, that appear grouped on an enlarged spadix forming a multiple, edible fruit.

Not particular regarding soil, although grows better in rich, well drained earth. Prefers partially shady location. Somewhat resistant to low temperatures.

Cultivated in tropics for its fruit which has a taste between pineapple and banana.

In gardening used to cover walls, columns, etc. Also to carpet the ground and as decorative potted indoor plant.

MONTANOA BIPINNATIFIDA

Montanoa bipinnatifida (Kunth) C. Koch.
Family: *Compositae.*
Geographical distribution: México.
Flowering period: late autumn-winter-spring.

Common name: DAISY TREE.
Propagation: by seed and cuttings.

Montanoa bipinnatifida.

Evergreen shrub up to 3 m high. Leaves opposite, pinnatifid to bipinnatifid, hairy. Limbs up to 45 cm long. Petioles up to 15 cm long. Flowers clustered in fragrant capitula up to 7 cm in diameter arranged in panicles. Disc-floret yellowish. Ligules white. Fruits in achenes.
Not particular about soil. Needs sunny site. Fast growing. Should be pruned after flowering.
Used in gardening individually or to form groups.

Montanoa bipinnatifida.

MONTANOA HIBISCIFOLIA

Montanoa hibiscifolia (Benth.) C. Koch.
Family: *Compositae.*   **Common name:** TREE DAISY.
Geographical distribution: South Mexico and from Guatemala to Costa Rica.
Flowering period: late autumn-early winter.   **Propagation:** by seed and cuttings.

Montanoa hibiscifolia.

Evergreen shrub up to 6 m high. Leaves opposite, palmalate-lobed, cordate, hairy. Limbs up to 45 cm long. Petioles up to 40 cm long. Flowers clustered in fragrant capitula up to 5 cm in diameter arranged in panicles. Disc-floret yellowish. White ligules. Fruits in achenes.
Tolerates most soils. Needs sunny site. Fast growing. Should be pruned after flowering.
Used in gardening individually or in groups.

MUSA RUBRA

Musa rubra Wall.
Family: *Musaceae.*
Propagation: by seed and division.

Geographical distribution: Burma.

Musa rubra.

Perennial, rhizomatous herb, with pseudostems up to 1.30 m high or more and 8 cm in diameter at base, tinted purple and black. Leaves arranged helicoidally, oblong-lanceolate, green, up to 2.30 m long, with reddish central vein, canaliculate above and prominent beneath. Flowers unisexual appearing in clusters along the reddish, pubescent rachis of erect terminal spike, protected by a red bract. The females in lower part and males in upper part. Calyx with five yellow lobes. Petal shorter than calyx. Fruits in berries, yellow, up to 9 cm long.

Needs rich, well drained soil and abundant moisture. Requires sunny site although accepts some shade. Must be protected from wind. Fast growing. Each pseudostem produces a bunch of small, unedible bananas and then dies. Used in gardening to form groups.

NANDINA DOMESTICA

Nandina domestica Thunb.
Family: *Berberidaceae.*
Flowering period: several times a year.
G. distribution: India through Eastern Asia.
Propagation: seeds, stem cutting and division.

Nandina domestica.

Evergreen shrub up to 2.5 m tall with thin, bamboo-like shoots.
Compound bi or tripinnate leaves up to 55 cm long. Oval or lanceolate
folioles up to 5.5 cm long. Small, white flowers clustered in terminal
panicles up to 30 cm or more long. Fruit in berries, red, up to 6 mm in
diameter.
It grows well in both the sun and shade. It requires well-drained, quite
humid soils. It grows slowly and stands cold weather. This is a very nice
plant whose foliage turns red in the autumn. It can grow alone or in
groups, and it is often grown as a potted plant.

NERIUM OLEANDER

Nerium oleander L. [*N. indicum* Mill.].
Family: *Apocynaceae.*
Flowering period: spring-summer-autumn.

Common name: COMMON OLEANDER.
G. distribution: Mediterranean countries.
Propagation: seeds and stem cutting.

Nerium oleander.

Evergreen shrub up to 4.5 m tall. Lanceolate leaves, up to 25 cm long, usually three per verticil. Pink flowers, clustered in terminal compound cymes. Fruit in difolicle up to 17.5 cm long.
It grows on most soils and withstands cold weather, drought and the proximity of the sea. It prefers sunny areas.
This is a very poisonous plant, although its sap has been used to treat some skin diseases.
This tree has been cultivated throughout history as a decorating indoor plant as well as in gardening in general.
There are several cultivars with simple, semidouble and double flowers in white, yellow, pink and red among other colors.

OCHNA SERRULATA

Ochna serrulata (Hochst.) Walp.
Family: *Ochnaceae.*
Flowering period: spring.

Common name: MICKEY-MOUSE PLANT.
Geographical distribution: South Africa.
Propagation: seeds and stem cutting.

Ochna serrulata.

Evergreen shrub up to 1.5 m tall. Narrowly elliptical leaves, acutely serrated, dark green above, paler beneath, up to 8 cm long. Flowers growing alone or in racemes with yellowish-green sepals that turn red in the fruit. Yellow petals that are soon shed. Fruit in pluridrupes in a widened, red receptacle.

It needs rich, very damp, well-drained loamy soils for fast growth. It needs the sun.

This shrub is seen in tropical and subtropical gardens. It is planted alone and in groups.

Ochna serrulata. Detail.

ODONTONEMA CALLISTACHYUM

Odontonema callistachyum (Schlechtend. et Cham.) O. Kuntze.
Family: *Acanthaceae.*
Flowering period: almost all the year.
G. distribution: Mexico and Central America.
Propagation: stem cutting.

Odontonema callistachyum.

Evergreen shrub up to 4.5 m tall. Opposite, sinuate, oblong to elliptical-ovate leaves up to 30 cm long. Pink to red flowers up to 3.5 cm long, clustered in raceme-like panicles, up to 45 cm long. Fruit in capsules.
It prefers well-drained soils rich in organic matter. It grows well in both the sun and shade. It is affected by drought. As it ages it becomes bare of leaves and for this reason it must be pruned short.
It is a very ornamental species that can grow alone or in groups.

ODONTONEMA STRICTUM

Odontonema strictum (Nees) O. Kuntze.
Family: *Acanthaceae.*
Flowering period: almost all the year.
Geographical distribution: Central America.
Propagation: stem cutting.

Odontonema strictum.

Evergreen shrub up to 1.8 m tall. Opposite, oblong, often undulate leaves, acuminate, up to 25 cm long. Scarlet, tubular flowers up to 3 cm long, clustered in raceme-like terminal panicles up to 40 cm long. Fruit in capsules.

It prefers rich, well-drained soils. It is affected by drought and although it accepts the sun directly it grows better in partly shaded areas. Young plants should be nipped back for a more compact growth. If it gets leggy, it must be pruned short.

It is cultivated alone or forming groups.

Odontonema strictum. Detail.

Pandanus utilis.

PANDANUS UTILIS

Pandanus utilis Bory.
Family: *Pandanaceae.*
Flowering period: spring.

Common name: COMMON SCREW PINE.
Geographical distribution: Madagascar.
Propagation: seeds and shoots.

Dioecious tree reaching heights of up to 18 m. From the lower parts of the trunk spring crutch-like aerial roots. Glaucous, sword-like leaves up to 1.40 m long and 10.5 cm wide, with spiny borders, arranged in rosettes at the end of the branches. Male, spadiciform inflorescences. Female inflorescences in capitula. The yellow-orange fruits come in drupes up to 4.5 cm long, grouped in globose (syncarp) infructescence, up to 25 cm in diameter.

It grows on most soils but prefers a warm spot with plentiful water. It can grow near the sea. It accepts the sun and shade equally well.

The fruit is edible and a fiber to make ropes, hats, baskets, and other objects is obtained from the leaves and roots. This is a very ornamental species generally seen in tropical and subtropical gardens. It is also seen indoors as a decorative plant in flowerpots.

Two aspects of Pandorea pandorana

PANDOREA PANDORANA

Pandorea pandorana (Andr.) Steenis.
[*Bignonia pandorana* Andr.].
Family: *Bignoniaceae.*
Geographical distribution: Malayan Archipelago, Australia.
Flowering period: winte-spring.
Propagation: by seed and cuttings.

Climber woody, evergreen. Leaves opposite, imparipinnate, with 3-9 folioles, up to 14 cm long. Folioles ovate to ovate-lanceolate, entire to densely crenate or dentate, up to 9 cm long, lighter beneath. Flowers hermaphrodite, clustered in terminal panicles up to 20 cm long. Corolla funnel shaped-campanulate, five-lobed, somewhat bilabiate, white with lobes and neck tinted purple, up to 19 mm long. Fruits in woody capsules. Prefers rich, well drained soil and somewhat shady site. Resistant to frost. Fast growing.
Used in gardening to cover walls, pergolas, fences, etc.

PARKINSONIA ACULEATA

Parkinsonia aculeata L.
Family: *Leguminosae.* **Geographical distribution:** Tropical America.
Common name: PARKINSONIA, JERUSALEM THORN.
Flowering period: spring through autumn. **Propagation:** seeds and stem cutting.

Parkinsonia aculeata.

Deciduous tree that can grow as much as 8 m tall, with a characteristic green trunk branches and spines up to 3 cm long. Compound, bipinnate leaves up to 40 cm or more long, with 2-3 pairs of pinnae joined to a very short rachis ending in a thorn. Very small folioles, oblong to obovate. Fruit in pods, light brown, up to 10 cm long.

It accepts most soils and direct contact with the sun. It withstands droughts well and it grows fast.

The foliage and fruit is given as food to cattle.

This is an ornamental tree seen in parks and gardens and used to line city streets. It is also used to form hedges.

PASSIFLORA EDULIS

Passiflora edulis Sims.
Family: *Passifloraceae.*
Common name: PURPLE GRANADINA, PASSION FRUIT.
Flowering period: late spring-summer-autumn.

Geographical distribution: Brazil.

Propagation: by seed and cuttings.

Passiflora edulis.

Climber evergreen, with stems obtusely angular, glabrous. Leaves alternate, trilobate, glabrous, serrate, up to 20 cm long or more. Flowers hermaphrodite, solitary, in leaf axils, up to 8 cm in diameter, subtended by three serrate bracts, up to 2.5 cm long. Sepals and petals white, often with purple tints. Filaments of crown white with base tinted purple. Fruits in berries, globular-oblong, purple when ripe, up to 5-6 cm in diameter. Prefers good quality soils, well drained. Needs sunny situation. Fast growing.
Cultivated in tropical and subtropical areas for its fruit whose pulp is eaten fresh or used in preparing juice, jams, soft drinks, etc.
In gardening it is used to cover walls, pergolas, etc.

PASSIFLORA MOLLISSIMA

Passiflora mollissima (HBK) L.H. Bailey.
Family: *Passifloraceae.*
Geographical distribution: Venezuela to Bolivia.
Propagation: by seed and cuttings.

Common name: BANANA PASSION FRUIT.
Flowering period: nearly year round.

Passiflora molissima.

Climber evergreen with axillary tendrils and stems dense and finely tomentose, cylindrical. Leaves alternate, three-lobed, with acute lobes and margins serrate-dentate, pubescent beneath, up to 14 cm long. Flowers hermaphrodite, solitary, in axils of leaves, up to 9 cm in diameter, subtended on three bracts. Five sepals and five petals pink in colour, joined at the base to form a tube up to 7 cm long, green. Crown is reduced to a band of purple, tuberculate. Stamen, five, joined to column bearing ovary and only separate in upper part of this column. Styles, three. Fruits in berries, oblong-ovoid, like a banana, yellow.
Prefers top quality soils with good drainage. Requires sunny site. Fast growing.
Fruit edible, giving top quality juice.
Used in gardening to cover walls, pergolas, etc.

PASSIFLORA TRIFASCIATA

Passiflora trifasciata Lem.
Family: *Passifloraceae.*
Flowering period: autumn-winter.

Geographical distribution: Peru.
Propagation: by seed and cuttings.

Passiflora trifasciata.

Climber evergreen. Leaves alternate, three-lobed, up to 22 cm long. Limbs green above, with yellowish-green colour along veins, with purple tones on young leaves, and reddish to violet beneath. Flowers hermaphrodite, in groups of two in axils of leaves, up to 3.5 cm in diameter. Sepals and petals greenish white. Crown whitish, with outer ring formed by filaments arranged radially. Stamens and styles bent downwards.

Prefers fertile, well drained soils. Can live in bright sun as well as in shade. Fast growing.
Used in gardening to cover walls, etc.

PAVONIA SEPIUM

Pavonia sepium St.-Hil.
Family: *Malvaceae.*
Geographical distribution:
South America.
Flowering period: almost throughout the year.
Propagation: seeds and stem cutting.

Pavonia sepium.

Evergreen shrub up to 2.5 m tall. Ovate to oblong-ovate, cuneate, serrated, acuminate, hairy leaves, up to 20 cm long. Yellow, solitary flowers that sometimes have the petals apically joined. Sepals and involucral bracts up to 9 mm long. Petals up 12-18 mm long. Fruit in schizocarps, with five mericarps provided with three erect thorns. It prefers light, well-drained soils rich in organic matter. It requires a partly shady area to grow well. It grows fast. This shrub is used in tropical and subtropical gardens and it can be planted alone or in groups.

PERSEA AMERICANA

Persea americana Mill. [*P. gratissima* C. F. Gaertn.].
Family: *Lauraceae.*
Geographical distribution: Tropical America.
Common name: AVOCADO TREE.
Propagation: seeds and grafting.

Evergreen tree up to 18 m tall or more. Oblong-lanceolate or elliptical-lanceolate to ovate or obovate leaves up to 25 cm long or more. Small, greenish flowers clustred in axilar or terminal panicles. Fleshy, large, piriform fruit in drupes, ovoidal or spherical, green, brown or purple in color, with a large seed.
Var. americana. This is the typical variety whose leaves do not release an anise scent when crushed. This variety includes the Antillean and Guatemalan races.
Var. drymifolia (Schlechtend. et Cham.) S. F. Blake. The leaves of this variety release anise scent when crushed. This variety includes the Mexican race. This species prefers deep, rich well-drained soils. It does not accept heavy, humid soils. It stands cold weather more than the mango tree. Its twigs are brittle, and for this reason it grows better in areas protected from the wind.

Persea americana.

The avocado tree is cultivated for its fruit in several parts of the world, such as in Mexico, Central and South America, The West Indies, Hawaii, Israel, Florida, California, India, the Canary Islands, Granada (Spain), etc. The avocado contains abundant vegetal oil, as well as an important number of proteins, vitamins and minerals, all of which give it a high nutritional value. It is eaten straight from the tree, in salads and in many varied ways. There are several cultivars that produce their fruits at different times of the year, such as those of 'Fuerte' and 'Hass'.

It is used as a shade and fruit tree in private gardens.

PETREA VOLUBILIS

Petrea volubilis L.
Family: *Verbenaceae.*
Common name: QUEEN'S-WREATH.
Geographical distribution: Central America, Mexico, West Indies.
Flowering period: almost all year.   **Propagation:** by seed and cuttings.

Petrea volubilis.

Climber woody or sub-shrub deciduous. Leaves opposite, entire or undulated, ovate, elliptical or oblong, acute, acuminate, obtuse or emarginated, very rough, like sand paper when mature, up to 20 cm long. Petioles short, up to 1 cm long. Flowers hermaphrodite, pale lilac to purple, up to 4 cm in diameter, clustered in pendulous, axillary racemes, up to 45 cm long. Calyx same colour as corolla, but usually paler. Corolla falls off after a few days, calyx remains for a long time. Fruits in drupes. Not particular about soil. Needs bright sun. Drought-resistant. Slow growing.
One of the most beautiful flowered climbers. Used to cover walls, pergolas, etc.

PHOENIX DACTYLIFERA

Phoenix dactylifera L.
Family: *Palmae.*
Propagation: seeds and shoots.

Common name: DATE PALM.
Geographical distribution: Arabia and Northern Africa.

Phoenix dactylifera.

Dioecious palm with slender trunk up to 30 m tall, sprouting at the base and covered for many years with the sheaths of shed leaves. Pinnate, glaucous, grayish-green leaves, up to 6 m long. The inflorescences appear among the leaves with small, yellowish flowers. Fruit (dates) in drupes, cylindrical to oblong-ellipsoidal, edible, up to 7.5 cm long.

It grows well on most soils and stands periods of drought. It requires the sun and grows fast. It can easily stand temperatures as cold as −9º C without coming to any harm.

Dates constitute one of the staple food elements in North African and Arabian countries. The main producers are Egypt, Iran and Iraq.

The date palm tree is also used for decoration purposes, growing in parks, gardens and in streets.

PHOENIX RECLINATA

Phoenix reclinata Jacq.
Family: *Palmae.*
Propagation: seeds and shoots.

Common name: SENEGAL DATE PALM.
Geographical distribution: Tropical Africa.

Phoenix reclinata.

Dioecious palm with multiple trunks that start from the base and reach a height of 7.5 m or more. Pinnate, gracefully arched leaves up to 3.5 m long. Orange, spiny petioles. Lanceolate pinnae, up to 70 cm long and 2.5 cm wide, acuminate. The inflorescences arise among the leaves, up to 1.5 m long, provided with unisexual, yellowish flowers. Oblong-ellipsoidal, red-orange to black fruits, up to 1.8 cm long.

It is not too demanding concerning the soil and prefers sunny areas. It grows fast and can safely stand temperatures as cold as −7º C.

With the sap of this palm an alcoholic beverage is made in Africa. The fibers of the trunks are used to make brushes and brooms. The core of the leave crowns is eaten by African natives.

It is used in gardening alone and to make screens and hedges.

Phoenix roebelenii.

PHOENIX ROEBELENII

Phoenix roebelenii O'Brien.
Family: *Palmae.*
Geographical distribution: Laos.

Common name: PYGMY DATE PALM.
Propagation: seeds.

Dioecious palm with a slender, single or multiple trunk 1.8 m tall and more. Pinnate leaves up to 1.2 m long. Narrowly lanceolate pinnae up to 35 cm long and up to 1.3 cm wide. The inflorescences grow among the leaves, up to 80 cm long, with yellowish, unisexual flowers.
Blakish fruits, up to 1.2 cm long.
It prefers rich, very damp soils. It requires partly shady areas, although it admits direct contact with the sun. It grows slowly and can withstand temperatures as low as −7º C without problems.
This is a very ornamental palm, used as indoor plant in courtyards. It is also used in gardens, either alone or forming groups.

PHYMOSIA UMBELLATA

Phymosia umbellata (Cav.) Kearn. *[Sphaeralcea umbellata* (Cav.) G.Don].
Family: *Malvaceae.*
Flowering period: autumn-winter.

Geographical distribution: Mexico.
Propagation: by seed and cuttings.

Phymosia umbellata.

Shrub or small tree evergreen up to 6 m high. Leaves simple, palmate-lobed, densely pubescent, with 3-5-7 lobes not deep, sinuate-dentate. Limbs up to 16.5 cm long. Petioles of similar length. Flowers hermaphrodite, clustered in umbellate cymes. Caliculus formed by three separate bracts. Corolla red-pink in colour, formed by five petals. Stamens joined in a tubular column. Fruits in schizocarps.
Not particular regarding soil. Prefers sunny location.
In gardening used individually or to form groups.

PHYTOLACCA DIOICA

Phytolacca dioica L.
Family: *Phytolaccaceae.*
Flowering period: spring-summer.

Common name: OMBU.
Geographical distribution: South America.
Propagation: seeds.

Dioecious tree with persistent or semipersistent leaves, reaching heights of up to 20 m. It has a very thick trunk, wider at the base. Elliptical or ovate leaves, 25 cm long or more. Unisexual flowers, clustered in suberect or pendular racemes, up to 15 cm long. Fleshy, yellowish fruit.
It accepts most soils and withstands strong winds. Can grow near the sea. Fast growing.
The ombu is greatly appreciated in Argentina, where it often appears in the lyrics of popular songs. Its roots have medicinal properties.
It is used as a shade tree. When used to line streets its powerful roots may uplift the pavement.

127

Phytolacca dioica.   *Pithecoctenium echinatum.* ▶

PITHECOCTENIUM ECHINATUM

Pithecoctenim echinatum (Jacq.) K. Schum. *[P. muricatum* Mo. ex DC.].
Family: *Bignoniaceae.*   **Common name:** MONKEY'S COMB.
Geographical distribution: Cuba, Jamaica and from Mexico to Brazil and Paraguay.
Flowering period: spring.   **Propagation:** by seed and cuttings.

Climber woody, evergreen, with angular branches. Leaves opposite,
3-foliolate or 2-foliolate with terminal foliole converted into tripartite
tendril. Folioles broadly ovate to suborbicular, up to 10 cm long. Flowers
hermaphrodite, clustered in terminal racemes up to 20 cm long. Corolla
tubulose-funnel shaped, somewhat bilabiate, pubescent, white with yellow
throat, up to 5 cm long. Tube elbowed and limb five-lobed. Fruits in
capsules, muricate, spiny, up to 15 cm long.
Accepts most soils. Needs sunny location.
Used in gardening to cover pergolas, walls, etc.

128

PITTOSPORUM TOBIRA

Pittosporum tobira (Thunb.) Ait.
Common name: JAPANESE PITTOSPORUM.
Flowering period: late winter-spring.

Family: *Pittosporaceae.*
Geographical distribution: China, Japan.
Propagation: by seed, cuttings and grafting.

Pittosporum tobira.

Shrub or small tree evergreen up to 5.5 m high. Leaves alternate or pseudoverticilate, obovate, with apex obtuse, coriaceous, thick, with margins revolute, dark green, glossy above and paler beneath, up to 11.5 cm long. Flowers hermaphrodite, pentamerous, fragrant, up to 2 cm in diameter, in terminal, umbellate racemes. Corolla white to yellowish-white, up to 8 mm long. Fruits in capsules, ovoid or almost triangular, up to 1.5 cm long, pubescent.
Not particular about soil. Prefers sunny location. Salt-tolerant so it is recommended for coastal gardens.
Used in gardening individually, to form groups or for hedges.

PITTOSPORUM UNDULATUM

Pittosporum undulatum Venten.
Common name: VICTORIA BOXWOOD, MOCK ORANGE.
Flowering period: late winter-summer.

Family: *Pittosporaceae.*
G. distribution: Australia.
Propagation: by seed and cuttings.

Evergreen tree up to 12 m high. Leaves alternate or pseudoverticilate, oblong to lanceolate, coriaceous, with revolute margins, undulated, dark green, glossy above and paler beneath, up to 15 cm long. Petioles short. Flowers hermaphrodite, white, fragrant, up to 15 mm in diameter, in terminal, umbellate racemes. Corolla up to 8 mm long. Fruits in capsules subglobose, orange when ripe, up to 1.5 cm in diameter.

Pittosporum undulatum.

Not particular regarding soil. Prefers sunny site. Salt-tolerant so recommended for coastal gardens. Fast growing. Resistant to frost. Used in gardening to form hedges, screens and as a shade tree.

PLUMBAGO AURICULATA

Plumbago auriculata Lam. *[P. capensis* Thunb.]. **Family:** *Plumbaginaceae.*
Common name: PLUMBAGO, LEADWORT. **Geographical distribution:** South Africa.
Flowering period: nearly year-round. **Propagation:** by seed and cutting.

Plumbago auriculata.

Shrub evergreen, semi-climber. Leaves alternate, entire, simple, oblong or oblong-spathulate, up to 8.5 cm long. Flowers blue or white, up to 4 cm long, in short spikes. Corolla salverform with long, slender tube, and limb five-lobed, up to 2.5 cm in diameter. Fruits in capsules.
Not demanding about soil. Needs strong sun, although tolerates partial shade. Sensitive to frost. Somewhat drought-resistant. Fast growing.
In South Africa some people think it has medicinal and magic properties. Its ground root is used to cure headaches and injuries.
In gardening used to cover walls, to form hedges, etc.

PODRANEA BRYCEI

Podranea brycei (N.E.Br.) T. Sprague *[Tecoma brycei* N.E.Br.; *Pandorea brycei* (N.E.Br.) Rehd.].
Family: *Bignoniaceae.* **Geographical distribution:** Zimbabwe.
Flowering period: nearly year-round. **Propagation:** by seed and cuttings.

Shrub climber evergreen. Leaves opposite, imparipinnate, up to 18 cm long, with 9-13 folioles lanceolate to ovate, glabrous, entire to serrate, acuminate, up to 8 cm long. Flowers hermaphrodite, clustered in terminal panicles. Corolla funnel shaped-campanulate, somewhat bilabiate, purple with darker strias coming out of bottom of tube, up to 7.5 cm long and 6 cm in diameter. Throat and inside of the tube both hairy. Fruits in capsules, linear, coriaceous, up to 40 cm long or more, containing many winged seeds.
Prefers good quality soil. Requires sunny site. Somewhat drought-resistant. Fast growing.
Used in gardening to cover fences, pergolas, etc.

Two aspects of Podranea bryecei.

PODRANEA RICASOLIANA

Podranea ricasoliana (Tanfani) T. Sprague *[Tecoma ricasoliana* Tanfani; *Pandorea ricasoliana* (Tanfani) Baill.].

Family: *Bignoniaceae.*
Flowering period: nearly year-round.

Geographical distribution: South Africa.
Propagation: by seed and cuttings.

Shrub climber evergreen. Leaves opposite, imparipinnate, up to 25 cm long, with 9-13 folioles ovate, serrate, glabrous, acute or acuminate, up to 10 cm long. Flowers hermaphrodite, clustered in terminal panicles. Corolla funnel shaped-campanulate, somewhat bilabiate, pink with red strias coming from bottom of tube, up to 6 cm long and 6 cm in diameter. Throat and tube slightly hairy. Fruits in capsules, linear, up to 40 cm long or more, containing many winged seeds.
Prefers good quality soil. Requires sunny site. Somewhat drought-resistant. Fast growing.
Used in gardening to cover walls, pergolas, etc.

POLYSCIAS GUILFOYLEI

Polyscias guilfoylei (Bull) L.H.Bailey *[Aralia guilfoylei* Bull].
Family: *Araliaceae.*   **Geographical distribution:** Polynesia.
Propagation: normally, by cuttings.

◀ *Podranea ricasoliana.*   *Polyscias guilfoylei.*

Shrub evergreen, erect growing up to 6 m high. Leaves pinnate, up to 60 cm long or more. Folioles ovate to nearly orbicular, serrate, usually with white or yellowish margins, although these colours sometimes spread to other parts of the limb. Foliole terminal larger, up too 20 cm long or more.
Flowers small, clustered in umbels arranged in panicles (does not usually bloom when cultivated). Fruits in drupes.
Prefers rich, well drained soil. Accepts bright sun as well as shade.
Drought-resistant. Fast growing.
Used in gardening individually, in groups or for hedges.

PSIDIUM GUAJAVA

Psidium guajava L.
Family: *Myrtaceae.*
Fruiting period: autumn-winter-spring.

Common name: COMMON GUAVA.
Geographical distribution: Tropical America.
Propagation: seeds, stem cutting and grafting.

Psidium guajava.

Evergreen shrub or small tree up to 9 m tall. Scaly brown bark.
Quadrangular twigs. Ovate to oblong-elliptical leaves, up to 15 cm long,
with prominent veins beneath. White, single flowers or in small groups, up
to 3 cm in diameter. Fruit in berries, ovoid to pyriform, yellow when ripe.
It does not need special soils, and it requires sunny areas. It stands
droughts well.
The common guava is cultivated for its fruits in India, Brazil, Guyana,
Cuba and a little in Florida and the Canary Islands. Its vitamin C content is
from two to three times that of oranges. It is eaten straight from the tree
and it is used to make preserves, jams, juices and guava paste. The wood is
used in carpentry.
It can also be used as ornamental tree in parks and gardens.

PSIDIUM LITTORALE

Psidium littorale Raddi var. *longipes* (O. Berg.) Fosb. *[P. cattleianum* Sab.].
Family: *Myrtaceae.*
Geographical distribution: Brazil.
Propagation: by seed, cuttings and grafting.

Common name: PURPLE STRAWBERRY GUANA.
Flowering period: spring.

Shrub or small tree evergreen up to 6 m high. Bark greyish-brown. Leaves
elliptical to obovate, glabrous, opposite, cuneate, up to 8 cm long. Flowers
white, solitary, up to 2.5 cm in diameter. Fruits in berries, subglobose, up
to 2.5 cm in diameter, red-purple in colour, edible and taste similar to
strawberries.
Prefers well drained soils and abundant moisture. Needs sunny location.
Widely cultivated in tropical and subtropical areas for its fruit, which can
be eaten fresh or used in making jams. Its juice is used in soft drinks.
Also planted as ornamental tree in parks and gardens.

136

Psidium littorale.

PYROSTEGIA VENUSTA

Pyrostegia venusta (Ker-Gawl.) Miers *[P. ignea* (Vell.)
K. Presl; *Bignonia venusta* Ker-Gawl.; *B. ignea* Vell.].
Family: *Bignoniaceae.*   **Common name:** FLAME VINE.
Geographical distribution: Brazil, Paraguay.   **Flowering period:** nearly year-round.
Propagation: usually by cuttings and air layering.

Pyrostegia venusta.

Shrub climber evergreen. Leaves opposite, composite, with 2-3 folioles.
Tendrils filiform, tripartite. Folioles ovate, acuminate, up to 12 cm long.
Flowers hermaphrodite, red-orange, clustered in terminal and paniculate
axillary cymes. Corolla tubular-funnel shaped, curved, with reflexed lobes,
up to 6 cm long. Stamens exserted in fours. Fruits in capsules, linear, up to
30 cm long.
Not particular regarding soil, prefers fertile, well drained bed. Requires
sunny location. Sensitive to frost. Fast growing.
Used in gardening to cover pergolas, banks, walls, etc.

137

QUISQUALIS INDICA

Quisqualis indica L.
Family: *Combretaceae.*   **Common name:** RANGOON CREEPER.
Geographical distribution: Burma, Malayan Peninsula, Philippines, New Guinea.
Flowering period: late spring-winter-autumn.
Propagation: by seed, cuttings and air layering.

Qyuisqualis indica.

Shrub climber, woody. Leaves opposite, oblong to oblong-elliptical, acuminate, up to 12 cm long, hairy. Flowers hermaphrodite, fragrant, clustered in hanging spikes. Tube of calyx green, slender, up to 6 cm long or more. Corolla with five petals, whose outer surface is white with pink tints. The inside first is white in the morning; then changes to pink and finally is red. Nut-like, alate fruit contains one seed.
Not demanding about soil. Prefers sunny location, although accepts some shade. Fast growing.
Used in gardening to cover pergolas, walls, etc.

RAPHIOLEPIS UMBELLATA

Raphiolepis umbellata (Thunb.) Mak *[R. japonica* Siebold et Zucc.].
Family: *Rosaceae.*   **Geographical distribution:** Japan.
Flowering period: nearly all year.   **Propagation:** by seed, cuttings and grafting.

Shrub evergreen up to 3 m high. Leaves alternate, ovate-oblong to obovate, coriaceous, revolute, dark green above and paler beneath, entire to serrate, up to 9.5 cm long. Flowers white, fragrant, up to 1.5 cm in diameter, clustered in dense panicles. Fruits in pomes similar to drupes, bluish-black, subglobose, up to 9 mm long.
Prefers fertile, well drained soil. Thrives in strong sun, although it can be cultivated in shade. Slow growing.
In Japan a brown dye is obtained from the bark.
Used in gardening individually or to form groups and as potted plant.

Raphiolepis umbellata.

RHAPIS EXCELSA

Rhapis excelsa (Thunb.) A. Henry. [*R. flabelliformis* L'Hér. ex Ait.].
Family: *Palmae.*
Common name: BAMBOO PALM.
Geographical distribution: Southern China.
Propagation: seeds and division.

Dioecious palm with multiple, bamboo-like stems up to 3 m high, covered with a thick brown fiber. Palmate leaves, split almost as far as the base in 3 to 10 linear segments, with serrated margins and truncated, dentated apex, up to 34 cm long and 6 cm wide. The inflorescences appear among the flowers, with small unisexual flowers. Globose to ovoid fruits.
Has no particular soil preference. Prefers partly shady areas but can grow in sunny spots. Withstands the cold, down to temperatures of to −8º C.
This is a very decorative palm used as an indoor potted plant. Also grown as courtyard decoration and in and gardens to form groups and hedges.

Raphis excelsa.

Raphis humilis. ▶

RAPHIS HUMILIS

Rhapis humilis Blume.
Family: *Palmae.*　　　　**Geographical distribution:** Southern China.
Propagation: by seed and division.

Dioecious palm multiple, cane-like stems up to 4.5 m high or more, covered with brown fiber. Leaves palmate, divided nearly to the base in up to 24 linear segments, up to 50 cm long and 6 cm wide or more, with apex narrow, truncate and dentate. Inflorescences appear among the leaves with very small unisexual flowers. Fruits in berries.
Not demanding regarding soil. Prefers partially shaded spots, although allows planting in bright sun.
Very decorative, used in gardening to form groups and hedges. Also as indoor potted plant and in decorating patios.

Roystonea regia.

Monoecious palm reaching heights of 20 m or more, with an even, greyish white trunk, either of a uniform thickness all the way up or often narrowing from a swollen base to about the mid-point, whereupon it once again swells and then narrows down again as it nears the top. Pinnate, arched leaves, up to 3 m long, with the folioles joined to the rachis in several levels to form an almost globose crown. Very branched inflorescences. Unisexual, white flowers. Dark red to purple fruits, nearly globose to obovoid, up to 12 mm long.
It is very affected by cold weather. It grows fast in rich damp soils in tropical areas. In subtropical areas its growth is usually slower. It withstands the wind and the saline spray from the sea.
In Cuba the fruit is used to feed cattle. The trunk and leaves are used to build cabins.
Often used to line streets as well as in gardens in tropical and subtropical gardens. It is a species recommended for protected coastal gardens.

Shrub up to 1.80 m high, with angular, glabrous stems that are arched and hang gracefully. Leaves verticillate, linear-lanceolate to ovate, serrate, up to 2.5 cm long, reduced to scales on branches. Flowers hermaphrodite, red, clustered in axillary cymes at end of branches and stems. Corolla tubular, five-lobed, somewhat bilabiate, up to 2.5 cm long. Fruits in capsules.
Not demanding about soil. Prefers sunny situation, although can live in some shade. Drought resistant. Can grow near the sea.
Used in gardening to form groups or individually. Also as potted plant.

Russelia equisetiforme.

RUTTYA FRUTICOSA

Ruttya fruticosa Lindau.
Family: *Acanthaceae.*
Flowering period: nearly year-round.

Geographical distribution: Tropical East Asia.
Propagaction: usually by cuttings.

Ruttya fruticosa.

Shrub evergreen up to 3.5 m high. Leaves opposite, entire, acuminate, ovate, up to 8 cm long. Flowers hermaphrodite, clustered in cymes. Calyx pentapartite. Corolla bilabiate, up to 5 cm long, with upper lip emarginated and lower one trilobate, yellow, orange-red or scarlet, with a spot in dark red, brown or black at base of middle lobe of lower lip, also affecting base of lateral lobes. Stamens, two. Fruits in capsules.
Not demanding about soil. Prefers sunny site. Fast growing.
In gardening used as individual sample or to form groups.

SALVIA LEUCANTHA

Salvia leucantha Cav.
Family: *Labiatae.*
Flowering period: nearly all year.

Geographical distribution: Mexico.
Propagation: by seed and cuttings.

Salvia leucantha.

Shrub evergreen up to 1.30 m high or more, with stems and branches lanate. Leaves opposite, linear-lanceolate, acute, crenate, rugose and pubescent above and lanate beneath, up to 15 cm long and 3 cm broad. Flowers hermaphrodite, clustered in spike-shaped racemes up to 30 cm long or more. Calyx funnel-shaped covered with purplish pubescence. Corolla pubescent, bilabiate, up to 2 cm long, white with violaceous tones. Fruit formed by four nuculars.
Prefers well drained soil. Thrives in sunny, dry places.
Usually used in gardening to form groups or carpet areas.

SCHINUS MOLLE

Schinus molle L.
Family: *Anacardiaceae.*
Flowering period: almost throughout year.

Common name: PEPPER TREE.
Geographical distribution: Peruvian Andes.
Propagation: seeds and cutting.

Dioecious, evergreen tree up to 15 m tall, with pendular branches that make it resemble the weeping willow. Compound, pinnate leaves up to 25 cm long. Linear-lanceolate folioles up to 5 cm long. Unisexual, white-yellowish, small flowers, clustered in panicles. Fruit in drupes, spherical, pink to red, up to 7 mm in diameter.
It grows on most soils as long as they are not too humid. It requires sunny areas and stands drought. It grows fast.

144

Schinus molle.

The seeds are hot in flavor, similar to pepper. It has been used to replace pepper, hence its name. The resin is used in South America as chewing gum. The Peruvian indians prepare a beverage known as «Chicha de molle.»
It is widely used in gardening. It can be seen in squares, parks, as well as in streets and roads.

SCHINUS TEREBINTHIFOLIUS

Schinus terebinthifolius Raddi.
Family: *Anarcadiaceae.*
Common name: BRAZILIAN PEPPER TREE.
Flowering period: spring-summer.

Geographical distribution: Brazil.

Propagation: seeds and stem cutting.

Dioecious, evergreen or semievergreen shrub or tree, up to 10 m tall. Imparipinnate leaves up to 40 cm long, with 5-19 folioles. Oblong, serrated folioles up to 8 cm long. Unisexual, small, greenish-white flowers clustered in panicles. Fruit in drupes, spherical, red and up to 5 mm in diameter. This species accepts most soils as long as they are not too humid. It requires sunny areas and withstands drought. It grows fast.
The foliage and fruits are used to make Christmas wreaths. The resin was formerly used to make the «Mission Balsam».
This is a very ornamental tree cultivated in parks, gardens and used to line city streets.

Schinus terebinthifolius.

SENECIO PETASITIS

Senecio petasitis (Sims) DC.
Family: *Compositae.*
Geographical distribution: Mexico.
Propagation: by seed and cuttings.

Common name: CALIFORNIA GERANIUM.
Flowerig period: winter-spring.

Evergreen shrub reaching a height of 2.5 m or more. Branches and petioles hirsute-velutinous. Leaves alternate, ovate to suborbicular, lobate, hirsutellous above and with greyish tomentum beneath, up to 30 cm long or more, with lengthwise petioles. Flowers in capitula clustered in terminal panicles. Capitula about 1.5 cm long and 2 cm in diameter, with five yellow ligules and the disc brown. Fruits in achenes, with whitish pappus.
Not demanding about soil, although prefers fertile, well drained ones. Can live in bright sun as well as in shade. Fast growing.
Used in gardening individually and to form groups.

Senecio petasitis.

SOLANDRA MAXIMA

Solandra maxima (Sessé et Moç.) P.S.Green *[S. nitida* Zuccagni; *S. hartwegii* N.E. Br.].
Family: *Solanaceae.* **Common name:** GOLDEN CUP.
Geographical distribution: Mexico. **Flowering period:** nearly year-round.
Propagation: usually by cuttings or aerial layering.

Shrub climber, woody, evergreen. Leaves alternate, entire, coriaceous, elliptical, obtuse to shortly acuminate, up to 27 cm long, with long petioles. Flowers hermaphrodite, solitary in short clusters, funnel shaped. Calyx three or four-lobed, up to 10 cm long. Corolla yellow, changing to yellow-brown with age, with five broad purple strias on inside, five-lobed, with lobes ornate and reflexed, up to 20 cm long. Fruits in berries, globose.
Accepts most soils. Requires abundant water, although has certain tolerance to drought. Needs sunny location. Somewhat resistant to frost. Should be pruned to shape. Fast growing.
Used in gardening to cover pergolas, walls, etc.

Solandra maxima.

SOLANUM SEAFORTHIANUM

Solanum seaforthianum Andr.
Family: *Solanaceae.*
Geographical distribution: Tropical America.
Propagation: by seed and cuttings.

Common name: BRAZILIAN NIGHTSHADE.
Flowering period: nearly year-round.

Solanum seaforthianum.

Plant climber, evergreen. Leaves can run from simple to pinnatifid or pinnate, up to 7.5 cm long. Flowers blue to purple, clustered in side cymes. Corolla star-shaped, pentapartite, up to 2.5 cm in diameter. Fruits in berries, globose, scarlet in colour.
Not particular regarding soil. Can be planted in shade. Sensitive to cold. In gardening used to cover walls, pergolas, etc.

SOLANUM WENDLANDII

Solanum wendlandii Hook. F.
Family: *Solanaceae.*
Flowering period: late spring-summer-autumn.

Geographical distribution: Costa Rica.
Propagation: by seed and cuttings.

Solanum wendlandii.

Plant climber, woody, somewhat spiny. Leaves vary in shape and size. The inside ones are pinnate; the middle ones, three-lobed or trifoliate, and the upmost ones simple, oblong-acuminate. Flowers hermaphrodite in terminal racemes. Corolla blue-lilac up to 6 cm in diameter. Fruits in berries, globose to ovoid, up to 10 cm in diameter.
Accepts most soils. Needs sunny situation and abundant watering and fertilizing. Sensitive to frost. Fast growing.
Used in gardening to cover walls, pergolas, etc.

SPATHODEA CAMPANULATA

Spathodea campanulata Beauv.
Family: *Bignoniaceae.*
F. period: almost throughout the year.

Common name: TULIP TREE.
Geographical distribution: Tropical Africa.
Propagation: seeds, stem cutting and shoots.

Evergreen tree that in the Canary Islands sheds its leaves once a year, reaching heights of up to 20 m. Pinnate leaves up to 65 cm long, with ovate-lanceolate folioles, up to 12 cm long. Large, bell-like flowers up to 7 cm in diameter, scarlet with gold-yellow edge, clustered in terminal racemes. Fruit in oblong-lanceolate capsules, 15-20 cm long.
It grows well on most soils and stands drought. In rich soils with abundant water it grows fast. It requires contact with the sun to flower adequately. It is affected by freezing weather.
This is one of the most beautiful tropical trees. Before the flowers open they are filled with water; for this reason the tree is also known as the «fountain tree.» Wild canaries pierce the buds of trees and drink the water. This is a suitable tree for lining streets and avenues. It is also widely grown in public and private parks and gardens.

149

Spathodea campanulata.

SPHAEROPTERIS COOPERI

Sphaeropteris cooperi (F.J. Muell.) Tryon *[Alsophila cooperi* F.J. Muell.;
Cyathea cooperi (F. J. Muell.) Domin.].

Family: *Cyatheaceae.*

Geographical distribution: Australia.

Common name: AUSTRALIAN TREE FERN.

Propagation: by spores.

Spharopteris cooperi.

Tree fern up to 6 m high or more, with trunk covered with scales. These do not end in a hardened hair and they have all cells similar. Fronds tripinnate up to 3 m long. Pinnas oblong-lanceolate up to 75 cm long. Pinnules serrate. Sorus rounded.

Requires soil rich in organic matter, well drained and with plenty of moisture. Accepts bright sun, although prefers shady site. Little resistance to wind. In time of active growth, the trunk must be watered frequently. Fast growing.

Used in gardening individually or to form groups. Also as potted plant for decorating patios and interiors.

STRELITZIA NICOLAI

Strelitzia nicolai Regel et Körn.
Family: *Musaceae.*
Geographical distribution: South Africa.
Propagation: by seed, shoots and division.

Common name: BIRD OF PARADISE TREE.
Flowering period: nearly year-round.

Plant with woody trunk up to 8 m high. Leaves distichous similar to those of the banana plant, oblong, up to 3.4 m long, at end of trunk. The inflorescences grow from the axils of leaves. Floral scape short, with one or two boat-shaped bracts at its end, purple, up to 40 cm long, with the flowers inside them. Flowers hermaphrodite, with sepals white and petals blue. Fruits in capsules. Seeds oblong, black, up to 1 cm long, with a filamentous aril orange in colour.
Prefers soils rich in organic matter and abundant moisture. Thrives in sunny site, although accepts some shade.
In gardening used individually or in groups.

Strelitzia nicolai. ▶

STRELITZIA REGINAE

Strelitzia reginae Ait.
Family: *Musaceae.*
Flowering period: nearly year-round.
Common name: STRELITZIA, BIRD OF PARADISE.

Geographical distribution: South Africa.
Propagation: by seed, shoot and division.

Plant herbaceous perennial, rhizomatous, acaulescent, up to 1.50 m high. Leaves oblong-lanceolate, concave, somewhat glaucous beneath, up to 1.20 m long. Floral scape longer than leaves, with one or two boat-shaped bracts at its end, green with purple or red margins, up to 22 cm long, containing the flowers. These are hermaphrodite, with three slender sepals, orange or yellow and three petals, two of which are joined to form a sagittate organ (tongue) dark blue in colour, with a central channel containing the stamens and style. Fruits in capsules. Seeds black, somewhat globose, with filamentous orange aril.

Prefers soils rich in organic matter and with abundant moisture. Requires sunny location, although accepts some shade. Slow growing. Used in gardening individually or to form groups. Also cultivated for cut flowers.

Strelitzia reginae.

SYAGRUS ROMANZOFFIANA

Syagrus romanzoffiana (Cham.) Glassman [*Arecastrum romanzoffianum* (Cham) Becc.]

Common name: QUENN PALM. **Family:** *Palmae.*

Geographical distribution: Brazil to Argentina. **Propagación:** seeds.

Syagrus romanzoffiana.

Monoecious palm up to 12-15 m high, with a grayish, ringed trunk. Pinnate leaves over 4.5 m long, arranged in different levels along the rachis. Branched inflorescences up to 90 cm that appear among the leaves, with small cream colored flowers. It has oval yellow fruits approximately 2.5 cm long. Takes to any soil but prefers a sunny spot. Can grow near the sea. Fast growing. Easy to transplant. It substitutes the Royal Palm Tree in areas where the latter cannot be cultivated.

It is widely cultivated in tropical and subtropical gardens in groups or alone. Also used for lining streets.

SYZYGIUM JAMBOS

Syzygium jambos (L.) Alston. [*Eugenia jambos* L.].
Family: *Myrtaceae.*
Flowering period: spring-summer-autumn.

Common name: ROSE APPLE.
G. distribution: Southeast Asia.
Propagation: seeds and stem cutting.

Syzygium jambos.

Evergreen tree reaching heights between 9-12 m Lanceolate, opposite leaves, shiny green above, paler beneath, up to 18 cm long. Very short petioles. Greenish-white flowers up to 8 cm in diameter, with many long stamens that constitute the most striking part of this tree. The flowers are grouped in racemes with not too many flowers. Ovoid, yellow-creamish fruit, with rose-like scent, up to 4 cm long.

This tree prefers loam, well-drained, damp soils, and it needs sunny areas. Although the fruit is edible it is rather tasteless. It is used to make jams and candies. The wood is of good quality and the bark is used in dying and tanning. This is the tree of the good and bad which in the Bible had the fruits of immortality.

It is used as a decorative, shade-giving tree in parks and gardens.

TAMARINDUS INDICA

Tamarindus indica L.

Family: *Leguminosae.*　　　　　　　**Common name:** TAMARIND.

Geographical distribution: probably from India.

Flowering period: late summer-autumn.　　**Propagation:** by seed, cuttings and grafting.

Tamarinus indica.

Tree with persistent leaves, up to 24 m high. Leaves paripinnate, up to 13 cm long. Folioles oblong, with apex obtuse or emarginated, up to 2.5 cm long. Flowers hermaphrodite, light yellow, up to 3.5 cm in diameter, clustered in terminal racemes, with few flowers. Petals with red veins. Fruit in legumes indehiscent, oblong, flat, brown, somewhat constricted, up to 15 cm long. Prefers rich, deep soils with abundant moisture. Susceptible to frost.

The tamarind is cultivated for its fruit, which contains a bitter, edible pulp. This pulp is used to prepare chutneys and spices, soft drinks, sweets and jams, and in medicine as it is carminative, laxative and antiscorbutic. The wood is used in carpentry.

Used a shade tree in gardens and parks and to line city streets.

TECOMA ALATA

Tecoma alata DC. [*T. smithii* W. Wats.].
Family: *Bignoniaceae.*   **Flowering period:** almost the entire year.
Propagation: seeds and stem cutting.

Tecoma alata.

Evergreen shrub reaching heights of up to 3 m. Imparipinnate, compound leaves with 11-17 oblong, acute, serrated folioles up to 3.2 cm long. Yellow flowers with reddish hues, tubular to funnel-shaped, up to 5 cm long, clustered in panicles up to 20 cm long. Fruit in brown linear capsules up to 10 cm long. It does not require special soils and grows best in sunny areas. It must be well watered during the summer. It is affected by cold weather. It is used in gardening, both alone and forming groups.

Tecoma alata. Detail.

TECOMA STANS

Tecoma stans (L.) HBK. [*Bignonia stans* L.].
Common name: BIGNONIA AMARILLA, SAÚCO AMARILLO.
Family: *Bignoniaceae.*   **G. distribution:** West Indies and from Mexico to Peru.
F. period: nearly year-round.   **Propagation:** seeds and stem cutting.

Tecoma stans.

Evergreen shrub up to 6 m tall. Imparipinnate leaves with 5-11 folioles up to 10 cm long, lanceolate to ovate-oblong, serrated. Yellow, bell-like flowers, 5 cm long, grouped in racemes. Fruit in linear capsules, 20 cm long and 6 mm wide. Alate seeds. It grows on most soils. It is more attractive if pruned short. It prefers sunny areas and grows fast.
When it flowers it is a very beautiful tree. It is widely used in gardens both alone and in groups.

Tecoma stans. Detail.

TECOMARIA CAPENSIS

Tecomaria capensis (Thunb.) Spach *[Tecoma capensis* (Thunb.) Lindl.].
Family: *Bignoniaceae.*   **Geographical distribution:** South Africa.
Flowering period: nearly year-round.
Propagación: by seed, cuttings and air layering.

Tecomaria capensis.

Shrub semi-climber, woody, evergreen. Leaves opposite or in groups of three, imparipinnate, up to 15 cm long. Folioles serrate, elliptical to ovate, orbicular or rhomboidal, up to 5.5 cm long. Flowers hermaphrodite, red-orange to scarlet, up to 5.5 cm long, clustered in terminal racemes. Fruits in capsules, linear, up to 5 cm long.

Not particular about soil, although grows better in rich ones with adequate moisture. Drought resistant. Prefers sunny spots. Fast growing. Can grow near the sea. Used to cover walls, pergolas, etc. and to form hedges. Regular pruning keeps it shrub-shaped.

Tecomaria capensis. Detail.

TERMINALIA CATAPPA

Terminalia catappa L.
Geographical distribution: Malayan Peninsula.
Floweing: spring-summer-autumn.

Common name: TROPICAL ALMOND.
Family: *Combretaceae.*
Propagation: seeds.

Deciduous tree reaching heights averaging 18-24 m. Its branches spread out horizontally. Entire, alternate, abovate leaves up to 30 cm long, clustered at the end of young branches. Before the leaves fall they become red, lending the tree a very nice aspect. Whitish, small flowers growing in terminal spikes up to 18 cm long. The almond-like fruits are 5-7 cm long, green with pale brown hues when ripe. Edible seeds.

Very hardy. Suitable for seaside gardens as it withstands the wind and salt.

The seeds are eaten raw and roasted. An almond-like oil is extracted from them. Unripe fruit. The green fruit is used to obtain tannin. The wood is used in construction. Used for lining streets as well as in coastal gardens. It is a handsome shade tree.

Terminalia catappa.

Terminalia catappa. Detalle.

TETRAPANAX PAPYRIFERUS

Tetrapanax papyriferus (Hook.) C. Koch *[Fatsia papyrifera* (Hook.) Benth et Hook. f.].
Family: *Araliaceae.*　　　　　**Geographical distribution:** China and Taiwan.
Common name: RICE PAPER PLANT.
Flowering period: autumn-early winter.
Propagation: by seed, shoots and root cuttings.

Tetrapanax papyriferus.

Shrub to small tree evergreen, with stolons but no thorns, up to 6 m high.
Leaves more or less verticillate, palmate-lobed, with lobes serrate, cordate-
ovate, densely pubescent beneath. Limbs up to 85 cm long. Petioles up to
95 cm long or more. Flowers hermaphrodite, small, white, arranged in
umbels grouped in a lanate, terminal panicle more than 1 m long. Fruits
in drupes, globular.
Not demanding about soil. Requires shady situation. Fast growing.
Cultivated in the Orient for manufacture of rice paper made with thin
sheets obtained from the pith of the stems.
Used in gardening to form groups.

161

Thunbergia coccinea.

THUNBERGIA COCCINEA

Thunbergia coccinea Wallich.
Family: *Acanthaceae.*
Propagation: by seed, cuttings and air layering.

Geographical distribution: India.
Flowering period: autumn-winter-spring.

Plant climber woody, evergreen. Leaves opposite, thick, glabrous, ovate to oblong, with base cordate or angular, dentate, dark green above and a little glaucous beneath, acuminate, up to 24 cm long. Flowers hermaphrodite, subtended by two large purple bracts, clustered in pendulous racemes up to 50 cm long. Corolla up to 2.5 cm long, with five scarlet, reflexed lobes and yellow throat. Fruits in capsules.
Prefers good quality, well drained soils. Requires sunny location.
Used in gardening to cover walls, pergolas, etc.

Thunbergia coccinea.

THUNBERGIA GRANDIFLORA

Thunbergia grandiflora (Roxb. ex Rottl.) Roxb.
Family: *Acanthaceae.*
Flowering period: nearly year-round.

Geographical distribution: India.
Propagation: usually by cuttings.

Thunbergia grandiflora.

Climbing plant, woody, evergreen. Leaves opposite, broadly ovate, rough, with margins dentate or angularly lobed, palmativeined, with 5-7 veins. Petioles up to 6.5 cm long. Limbs up to 20 cm long. Flowers hermaphrodite blue, solitary or usually clustered in pendulous racemes. Corolla up to 7.5 cm in diameter, with five lobes rounded, somewhat bilabiate. Tube up to 3.5 cm long, with yellow throat. Fruits in capsules. Grows better in good quality soil with easy drainage. Prefers sunny location. Fast growing. Somewhat resistant to cold.
Used in gardening to cover walls, fences, pergolas, etc.

TIPUANA TIPU

Tipuana tipu (Benth.) O. Kuntze.
Family: *Leguminosae.*
Flowering period: spring-summer.

Common name: ROSE WOOD, TIPA.
Geographical distribution: Southern Brazil to Bolivia.
Propagation: seeds.

Tipuana tipu.

Briefly deciduous tree that may reach heights of up to 30 m. Imparipinnate leaves 30 cm or more long. Folioles in 6-11 pairs, elliptical, obovate or oblong, up to 6 cm long and up to 2 cm or more wide, emarginate. Yellow-orange flowers, clustered in axilar racemes shorter than the leaves. Fruit in alate pods, up to 8.5 cm long.
It prefers rich, well-drained soils and it requires sunny areas. It withstands drought and grows fast. It can be transplanted without problems when adult.
The wood of this tree, known as rosewood is used for making cabinets. The bark is used in tanning and home medicine. The foliage is used as fodder. This tree is used in subtropical areas as a shade-giving tree in parks and gardens and to line streets.

164

TRACHYCARPUS FORTUNEI

Trachycarpus fortunei (Hook.) H. Wendl.   **Family:** *Palmae.*
Geographical distribution: Northern Burma and Central-eastern China.
Common name: WINDMILL PALM.   **Propagation:** seeds.

Trachycarpus fortunei.

Polygamous - monoecious palm up to 12 m tall. Slender trunk covered with brown fibers produced from the sheaths of old leaves. The fibers are loose and undulate. Fan-like, dark green or sometimes slightly glaucous leaves. Blades 50-85 cm long, divided into several narrow segments to their middle part, and often to the base. Petioles up to 110 cm long, with toothed borders. Small, yellow flowers clustered in panicular inflorescences up to 60 cm long. Kidney-like fruit, blue when ripe, up to 12 mm in diameter.
It stands well cold weather to temperatures as cold as –11º C. It grows well on most soils as long as they are well-drained and rich.
The fibers are used to make ropes and thick weaves.
It is used in gardening and as an indoor plant.

TRITHRINAX ACANTHOCOMA

Trithrinax acanthocoma Drude.   **Family:** *Palmae.*
Geographical distribution: Southern Brazil.   **Propagation:** seeds.

Hermaphroditic palm up to 4.5 m tall, with the trunk covered by a fibrous tissue. The sheaths of leaves are provided with long thorns on the borders. Palmate, orbicular leaves, glaucous beneath, up to 1.8 m long, divided into approximately 40 bifid segments. Thornless petioles up to 90 cm long. The inflorescences appear among the leaves, paniculate, with small flowers. Globose, yellow-creamish fruits up to 2.5 cm in diameter.

Trithrinax acanthocoma.

It grows on most soils, and prefers sunny areas. It grows slowly and is rather resistant against cold weather.

It is used in gardening thanks to its ornamental aspect.

WASHINGTONIA FILIFERA

Washingtonia filifera (L. Linden) H. Wendl.
Family: *Palmae.*
Common name: DESERT FAN PALM.
Geographical distribution: California, S.W. United States, Mexico.
Propagation: seeds.

Hermaphroditic palm reaching heights of up to 24 m when growing wild, but not taller than 15 m when it is cultivated. Massive, greyish trunk. Palmate leaves. Petioles with spiny margins up to 1.5 m long. Grey-green blades up to 2 m in diameter, divided into numerous erect segments

166

Washingtonia filifera.

covered with many threadlike, white fibers. Branched inflorescences with pendular branches that appear among the leaves. Small, white flowers. Ovoid, small, brown fruit in drupes.

A hardy palm that grows fast if given plenty of water. It prefers sunny areas and withstands the proximity of the sea.

The natives of the places where this palm grows originally used the leaves to make cabins, sandals and baskets. The petioles were used to make furniture and similar objects. The medulla of the spadix was used to make fire by friction and the fruits were used as food.

This palm is used to line city streets as well as in parks and gardens.

Washingtonia filifera.

WASHINGTONIA ROBUSTA

Washingtonia robusta H. Wendl. [*W. sonorae* S. Wats; *W. gracilis* S. Parisch.].
Family: *Palmae.*
Common name: THREAD PALM.
Geographical distribution: Mexico.
Propagation: seeds.

Hermaphroditic palm averaging heights of over 25 m, with a thinner trunk than W. filifera. Palmate leaves. Petioles with spiny margins up to 1.5 m long. Bright green blades up to 1.8 m in diameter, divided into many gracefully arched segments, without threadlike fibers, except for the young palms. Branched inflorescences with pendular branches that appear among the leaves. White flowers. Ovoid, small, brown fruit in drupes.
It grows on most soils and requires direct contact with the sun. If provided with abundant water it grows fast. The local Indians taught the Spanish conquerors to eat the typical palm bud, a habit that then led to the destruction of many palm woods. The leaves were used in their funerals. Used to line streets and in gardening in general.

Washingtonia robusta.

YUCCA ALOIFOLIA

Yucca aloifolia L.
Family: *Agavaceae.*   **Common name:** YUCA, SPANISH BAYONET.
Geographical distribution: West Indies, Southeast United States and Mexico.
Flowering period: spring-summer-autumn.   **Propagation:** by seed and stem cutting.

Yucca aloifolia.

Tree with single or multiple trunk, up to 7 m tall. Leaves arranged in
rosettes, thick, fleshy, dagger-like, 75 cm long and 6 cm wide, with a thorn
at the end. Inflorescences in panicles up to 60 cm long, with white,
fragrant flowers about 5 cm long. Black fruit in berries.
A very hardy palm, growing well on most soils. It requires little water and
withstands the proximity of the sea. It prefers sunny areas.
It is very widely used in gardening, on lawns and rockeries, etc.

ZANTEDESCHIA AETHIOPICA

Zantedeschia aethiopica (L.) K. Spreng. *[Richardia africana* Kunth].
Family: *Araceae.*
Geographical distribution: South Africa.
Propagation: by seed and division.

Common name: CALLA LILY.
Flowering period: nearly year-round.

Zantedeschia aethiopica.

Rhizomatous, acaulescent herbaceous plant, up to 90 cm high or more. Leaves entire, sagittate, with cordiform base. Petioles long. Limbs green, glossy, up to 45 cm long and 25 cm broad. Flowers unisexual, small arranged along a cylindrical spadix yellow in colour, the male ones in the upper part and females ones in lower part. Spathe white, funnel-shaped, with short tube and curved limb, up to 25 cm long. Floral scape surpasses height of leaves. Fruits in berries.
Prefers rich soil with abundant moisture. Thrives when cultivated in partially shady spot. Fast growing.
The first South African settlers used it to treat gout and rheumatism.
Very popular in gardening to form groups, bordering ponds and as water plants. Also used for cut flowers.

APPENDICES

BIBLIOGRAPHY

BAILEY, L. H.: *The Standard Cyclopedia of Horticulture,* 3 vols., 3639 p., The MacMillan Company, Nueva York, 1947.

BURKART, A.: *Las Leguminosas Argentinas Silvestres y Cultivadas,* 569, p., ACME AGENCY, Soc. de Resp. Ltda., Buenos Aires, 1952.

CEBALLOS, L., y RUIZ DE LA TORRE, J.: *Árboles y arbustos de la España peninsular,* 512 p., Instituto Forestal de Investigaciones y Experiencias y Escuela T. Superior de Ingenieros de Montes, Madrid, 1971.

CHITTENDEN, F. J. (Ed.): *The Royal Horticultural Society Dictionary of Gardening,* 3 vols., 2316 p., Oxford University Press, Oxford, 1977.

CHITTENDEN, F. J. (Ed.): *Supplement to the Royal Horticultural Society Dictionary of Gardening,* 1088 p., Oxford University Press, Oxford, 1979.

FONT QUER, P.: Diccionario de botánica, 1244 p., Editorial Labor, S. A. Barcelona, 1977.

GRAF, A. B.: *Exotica 3. Pictorial Cyclopedia of Exotic Plants,* 1834 p., Roehrs Company, E. Rutheford, 1970.

GRAF, A. B.: *Tropica. Color Cyclopedia of Exotic Plants and Trees,* 1136 p., Roehrs Company, E. Rutheford, 1981.

GUÍNEA LÓPEZ, E., y VIDAL BOX, C.: *Parques y jardines de España. Árboles y arbustos,* 413 p., Publicaciones del Ministerio de Educación y Ciencia, Madrid, 1969.

HOYOS, J.: *Flora tropical ornamental,* 430 p., Sociedad de Ciencias Naturales La Salle. Monografía n.º 24, Caracas, 1978.

HUCK, L. E., y TONGG, R. C.: *The Modern Tropical Garden,* 250 p., Tongg Publishing Company, Honolulú, 1970.

KUNKEL, G.: *Flowering Trees in Subtropical Gardens,* 346 p., Dr. W. Junk b.v., Publishers, La Haya, 1978.

LIBERTY HYDE BAILEY HORTORIUM: *Hortus Third,* 1290 p., MacMillan Publishing Co., Inc., Nueva York, 1978.

MECURRACH, J. C.: *Palms of the World,* 290 p., Harper and Brothers, Nueva York, 1960.

MENNINGER, E. A.: *Flowering Trees of the World,* 336 p., Hearthside Press Incorporated, Nueva York, 1962.

MOORE, H. E.: *The Major Groups of Palms and Their Distribution,* 115 p., L. H. Bailey Hortorium, Nueva York, 1973.

PALMER, E., y PITMAN, N.: *Trees of Southern Africa,* 3 vols., 2235 p., A. A. Balkema, Ciudad del Cabo, 1972.

PAÑELLA BONASTRE, J.: *Árboles de jardín,* 300 p., Oikos-tau, S. A. Ediciones, Barcelona, 1972.

Van der spuy, U.: *South African Shrubs and Trees for the Garden,* 215 p., Hugh Keartland Publishers, Johannesburgo, 1971.

Whitmore, T. C.: *Palms of Malaya,* 129 p., Oxford University Press, Oxford, 1979.

Wrigley, J. W., y Fagg, M.: *Australian Native Plants,* 448 p., Williams Collins Publishers Pty Ltd, Sidney, 1979.

GLOSSARY OF BOTANICAL TERMS

Above.– Upper side of leaves, opposite of beneath.

Acaulescent.– Lacking a distinct stem.

Aculeate, a.– Provided with prickles.

Acuminate, a.– Ending in a point.

Acute, a.– Any foliaceous organ (leaves, folioles, etc.) narrowed gradually and making an angle of less than 90.

Achene.– Dry fruit, indeshicent, monospermous.

Adaxial.– On the side of a lateral organ towards the axis or stem

Alkaloid.– Vegetal substance, basic and with strong physiological action.

Alate.– Winged or with wing-like appendages.

Ament.– Raceme resembling a spike, usually made up of unisexual flowers and pendulum most of the time.

Amentiform.– Similar to Ament.

Amplexicaul.– Stem-clasping.

Angular, a.– Provided with angles.

Anther.– Pollen-producing part of the stamen.

Apetalous.– Without petals.

Apiculate.– Ending in a short, sharp point.

Aril.– Additional covering formed on the seeds.

Articulate.– With one or more joints or points of apparent separation, usually marked by a swelling, line or abrupt change in colour.

Axil.– Higher angle formed by a lateral organ (leaf, bract, etc.), joining the caulinar in which it is inserted.

Axilar.– Placed on the axil.

Beneath.– Opposite of above in leaves, etc.

Berry.– Pulpous fruit, indeshicent, containing many or few seeds and without a real stone, such as seen in grapes.

Bifid, a.– Said of the organ (leaf, foliole, etc.) divided into two segments that do not reach halfway of its total length.

Bipinnatifid.– Pinnatifid leaf whose divisions in turn are bipinnatifid.

Biotype.– Synonymous of biological form.

Bipinnate, a.– Twice pinnate.

Blade.– Laminar part of the leaf.

Brachyblast.– Sprig with very short internodes, usually of limited growth with very close together leaves.

Bract.– Foliaceous organ, different from the leaf, associated with the flower or inflorescence.

Calyptra.– Kind of cap that protects the vegetative cone of the root. Also the structure formed as the result of the union of the petals and lobes of the calyx in the Eucalyptus flower.

Calyx.– Outer verticil of perianth, made up by the sepals.

Canaliculate.– Longitudinally channeled or grooved.

Capitulum.– Inflorescences made up of sessil flowers on a very short, wide axis.

Capsule.– Dry fruit, dehiscent, formed by the union of two or more carpels.

Carpellary leaf.– Each one of the units that make up the pistil.

Cincinnus.– Scorpioid cyme in which the twigs it consists of grow to the right and left alternatively.

Cone.– Inflorescence consisting of a central axis on which naked, unisexual flowers and the tectrix bracts are inserted. The cones grow on coniferous species such as pines, firs, etc.

Connivent.– Converging together, usually of organs with their bases separate and their appices approaching each other, not touching or fused.

Convolute.– Rolled together longitudinally.

Cordate, a.– Synonymous of cordiform.

Cordiform.– Heart-shaped.

Corolla.– Inner verticil of perianth, formed by the petals.

Corona.– Set of petaloid appendices between the stamen and the corolla.

Corymb.– Racemose, simple inflorescence characterized by peduncles that start from different heights, although the flowers are at the same level.

Corymbiform.– Corymb-shaped.

Crenate.– With shallow, rounded teeth.

Crenulate.– Diminutive of crenate.

Crenulate, a.– Festooned with small festoons.

Cultivar.– A distinct true-breeding race or form, established in cultivation.

Cultivate.– Cultivated variety. Group of cultivated plants easy to distinguish for their morphological and phisiological characteristics and that keep their characteristics when they reproduce sexually or asexually.

Cuneate, a.– Wedge-shaped.

Cyathium.– Inflorescence typical formation. The female flower reduced to one pistil and the male flowers reduced to one stamen.

Cyme.– Defined inflorescences whose axis end in a flower, as well as in the secondary lateral axes.

Deciduous, a.– With shedding leaves.

Decurrent.– Extending downwards beyond the point of insertion.

Dehiscent.– That opens.

Deltoid.– Broadly triangular and attached at the base.

Dentate.– With sharp teeth perpendicular to the margin.

Dichotomous.– Forking into two equal branches.

Digitate, a.– Said of the leaves, bracts, etc., divided into deep diverging lobes that start from a point, like the fingers in an open hand.

Dioecious, a.– Plants with unisexual flowers: the male and female flowers being on different plants.

Drupe.– Fleshy fruit, monocarpellate, indehiscent, with a stone inside it.

Ellipsoidal.– Having an elliptical profile.

Emarginate– Notched at the extremity.

Endocarp.– Inner layer of the pericarp.

Endosperm.– Reserve tissue of seed.

Ensiform.– Sword-shaped.

Evergreen, a.– With perennial leaves.

Exserted.– Refers to stamens that project beyond the corolla.

Face.– Uper surface of the leaf.

Festooned, a.– Bordered with festoons.

Filament.– Any thread-like body, especially the stalk of stamens supporting the anther.

Follicle.– Dry fruit, dehiscent, monocarpellate, that only opens along a single grooved line.

Foliole.– Foliaceous organ joined to the rachis of a leaf or its divisions.

Glabrous.– Hairless.

Glandular.– Provided with glands.

Glaucous.– Light green-bluish.

Gynoecium.– Group of the female organs of the flower.

Hermaphrodite.– Bisexual.

Hirsute.– With distinct hairs, often rather stiff or bristly.

Imparipinnate, a.– Used to describe a pinnate leaf that terminates in a foliole.

Indehiscent.– That which does not open.

Inflorescence.– Group of flowers, arranged in a determined form, each plant with its own characteristics.

Infrutescence.– Group of fruits proceeding from an inflorescence.

Infundibular.– Funnel-shaped.

Involute.– Rolled inwards or to the adaxial side.

Laciniate, a.– Divided into deep, narrow lobes.

Lanceolate.– Lance-shaped.

Legume.– A dry, dehiscent, mono-carpellate fruit, which opens along the ventral suture and the middle nerve, characteristic of the leguminosae.

Ligule.– A collarlike or tonguelike projection near the junction of sheath or petiole and blade.

Linear.– Long and narrow, with parallel, or almost parallel edges.

Lobular, a.– Divided into lobules.

Macroblast.– Long shoots which form or prolong the branches.

Mericarp.– Each of the parts into which a schizocarp divides.

Mesocarp.– Middle layer of the pericarp.

Monoecious, a.– Used to describe plants with unisexual femenine and masculine flowers on the same plant.

Mucronate, a.– Ending in a short point.

Muricate, a.– With thorns or spines.

Oblanceolate, a.– Used to describe laminas (leaves, petals, etc.) in the form of a lance, but in reverse, that is, with the wider part at the top, and the narrower part at the base.

Obovate, a.– Egg-shaped, with the wider part at the top.

Obtuse, a.– Foliar organ (bract, leaf, etc.) the edges of which form an obtuse angle at the top.

Orbicular.– Circular.

Ovoid.– Egg-shaped.

Palmate-lobed.– Palmately nerved leaf divided to the mid point into marked, more or less round lobes.

Palmatilobate.– Used to describe a foliaceous organ with palmate nervation, the bottom half of which is divided into very clear, almost round lobules.

Palmatifid.– Radially lobed more or less half way.

Palmatisect.– Midway between palmate and palmatifid.

Panduriform.– Guitar-shaped.

Panicle.– A branching raceme.

Paniculate.–Arranges in panicles.

Paripinnate.– Used to describe a pinnate leaf with an even number of folioles.

Peduncle.– Leaf-stalk of a flower or an inflorescence.

Pericarp.– The wall of the fruit. Usually made up of three layers, the external (epicarp), the internal (endocarp) and between them, the mesocarp.

Petiole.– Stalk that joins the blade of a leave with the stem.

Pinnate, a.– With the parts (veins, folioles, etc.) arranged along both sides of an axis, similar to the barbs on the shaft of a feather.

Pinnately parted.– Foliaceous organ with pinnate veins in which the divisions of the segments reach the central vein.

Pinnatipartite.– Pinnately lobed half to two thirds the depth of the lamina.

Pinnatifid.– Pinnately lobed more or less halfway.

Pinnule.– The second or third order divisions of a bi- or tripinnate leaf

Pistil.– Unit of the gynoecium consisting of ovary, style and stigma.

Pistillode.– Aborted pistil.

Polygamous, a.– Said of the plants with hermaphrodite and unisexual flowers on the same plant or on different ones.

Puberulent.– Minutely pubescent, the hairs soft and very short.

Pubescent.– Covered with soft, short, fine hairs.

Pyriform.– Pear-shaped.

Raceme.– Inflorescence formed by an axis with pedunculate flowers on both sides.

Racemose.– Group of fruits originating from an inflorescence.

Rachis.– Axis of an inflorescence or of a compound leaf.

Reflexed.– Bent sharply backwards.

Reniform.– Kidney-shaped.

Revolute.– Said of the leaves whose edges are turned inside down.

Salverform.– Having a slender tube that expands abruptly.

Sagittate.– Shaped like an arrow head.

Scandent.– Climbing, usually without special climbing organs.

Scape.– Leafless stem rising from a bulb, rhizome, etc, with flowers at its apex.

Schizocarp.– Dry, dehiscent fruit that breaks up in mericarps.

Sheath.– A more or less tubular structure surrounding an organ or part

Sheathing.– Forming a sheath.

Sepal.– Each one of the leaves of the calyx.

Serrated, a.– Synonymous of serrate.

Serrated, a.– Said of the foliaceous organs provided with sharp, clustered teeth along the edges, resembling a saw.

Sessile.– Without stem or base. A sessile leaf does not have a petiole.

Sinuous.– With sinuses.

Sorus.– A group or arrangement of sporangia in ferns (pl. sori).

Spadiciform.– Spadix-shaped.

Spadix.– Tassel with fleshy flowers, usually unisexual and surrounded by spathes.

Spathe.– Bract that wraps the spadix, sometimes large and reddish.

Spathulate.– Spoon-shaped.

Stamen.– Flower organ having pollinic sacs with the pollen.

Strobila.– Synonymous for cone.

Subulate.– Awl-shaped, narrow and gradually tapering to a fine point.

Syconium.– Fleshy fruits of the fig family consisting of a large receptacle.

Syconus.– Fruit of the plants of the Ficus genus. It is racemose with a fleshy receptacle with tiny fruits.

Syncarp.– Group of joined fruits either belonging to one flower or to different flowers.

Tannin.– Vegetal, astringent substances used in tanning and for making dyes.

Tassel.– Racemose, simple inflorescence with sessile flowers.

Thornless.– Without prickles or spines.

Tomentum.– Group of interwined hairs resembling goat's hair.

Toothed, a.– Said of foliaceous organs such as leaves and petals with edges resembling a saw, but with less sharp teeth.

Triad.– Group of three.

Truncate, a.– With the apex cut off.

Umbel.– Racemose inflorescence with an axis from whose end grow pedicels of the same length.

Umbellate.– Having umbels.

Umbelliform.– Umbel-shaped.

Unisexual.– Having only one sex.

Upper culm.– In palm trees, the extension of the trunk above the inflorescence, formed by the sheaths of the leaves.

Utricle.– Bladder-like, indehiscent fruit of certain plants.

Variegated.– Of various colours or varied constitution.

Velutinous.– Covered with fine, soft velvet-like hairs.

Verticillate, a.– Arranged in verticils.

Verticil.– Group of two or more organs (leaves, bracts, etc.) all growing at the same level. Whose edges form an acute angle.

INDICES

ALPHABETICAL INDEX
OF SCIENTIFIC NAMES

190

GENERAL INDEX

CANARY IS

LA PALMA

Punta del Mudo • El Mudo
Garafía
Faro de Punta Cumplida
Barlovento
Casas
Roque Farás
San Andrés y Sauces
Punta Izcagua
Garachico • Punta el Guincho
Puntagorda
Tinizara
Puntallana • Punta Salinas
Punta de la Laja
Tijarafe
Los Álamos
Las Tierritas
STA. CRUZ
DE LA PALMA
Punta el Moro •
Los Llanos de Aridane
Breña Alta
El Paso • Breña Baja
Todoque
Playa Nueva
Villa de Mazo
Las Manchas
Puerto Naos
Punta el Lajio
Malpases
Monte de Luna • Punta de Tigalete
Punta Vuelta del Toro
Las Caletas
Fuencaliente de la Palma
Punta de Fuencaliente

Punta

Cruz de las Bajas
Puerto de Vallehermoso
Loja del Infierno
Argamul
Agulo Lepe
Tazo
Vallehermoso
Los Picuchos
Hermigua
Alojera
Los Loros
Arure
Ntra.
de Guad
Los Manantiales
Calera • Valle Gran Rey
Molinito
Vueltas
Almácigos Alajero
El Cabrito
La Rajita
Quise
Punta Gor
Punta del Guinc
Santiago

LA GOME

Punta del Machuco
Bahía de las Calcosas
Echedo • Punta de Amacas
Monácal
Las Puntas
Valverde
Punta Negra
San Andrés
Bahía de los Pozos
Frontera
Bahía de los Reyes
Tigaday
Sabinosa
Tiñace
Isora • Punta de Ajones
Punta del Barbudo
Las Casas
Punta de Tejeda
La Restinga
Punta de los Frailes • Punta Restinga

EL HIERRO